Keeping Bees

Garden Farming Series

Keeping Bees

Peter Beckley

PELHAM BOOKS

First published in Great Britain by
Pelham Books Ltd
44 Bedford Square
London WC1B 3DU
1977
Paperback edition September 1982

British Library Cataloguing in Publication Data

Beckley, Peter
    Keeping bees.—2nd ed.
    1. Bee culture
    I. Title
    638'.1   SF525

    ISBN 0 7207 1436 2

Printed and bound in Great Britain by
Hollen Street Press Ltd, Slough

To Gladys, who started it all . . .
and to Fred Richards N.D.B., sometime County
Beekeeping Instructor for Devon and for Norfolk,
whose patience and essentially practical approach
to the craft, based on a lifetime's experience,
started many people on the road to successful
beekeeping.

Contents

Acknowledgements

Many people have been helpful in the writing of this book.

I would like to thank especially Rosemary Coups for typing and re-typing, and my wife for reading and re-reading, the manuscript—an arduous task they carried out with much forbearance.

Appreciation is also due to Elisabeth Downing for her help and encouragement and to Ted Downing for permission to use the conversion table reproduced here.

Thanks must also go to the countless, nameless beekeepers who, over a period of many years, have been so free with their knowledge and help.

Conversion Table

Metric and Imperial Equivalents

Imperial	Metric	Metric	Imperial
1 inch	2.54 cm	1 cm	0.39 in
1 foot	30.48 cm	1 cm	0.033 ft
1 yard	0.91 m	1 m	1.094 yds
1 mile	1.61 km	1 km	0.62 miles
1 sq yd	0.84 sq m	1 sq m	1.196 sq yds
1 cu yd	0.76 cu m	1 cu m	1.31 cu yds
1 pint	0.57 litre	1 litre	1.76 pints
1 gal	0.0056 cu m	1 cu m	219.97 gals
1 gal	4.55 litre	1 litre	0.22 gals
1 fl oz	28.4 ml	1 ml	0.035 fl oz
1 oz	28.35 g	1 g	0.035 oz
1 lb	0.45 kg	1 kg	2.20 lb
1 acre	0.405 hectare	1 hectare	2.47 acres
$x\,°F$	$\frac{5}{9}(x-32)\,°C$	$y\,°C$	$(\frac{9}{5}y+32)\,°F$

Metric abbreviations

cm	centimetre
m	metre
km	kilometre
ml	millilitre
g	gram
kg	kilogram

Introduction

More and more people are taking up the pleasant and rewarding hobby of beekeeping. It has been noticeable over the past few years that it is not only those who have recently retired who are doing so, but younger people who have a desire to produce something for themselves—a form of self-sufficiency.

Many would like to be more self-sufficient and produce that little extra, which when sold will supplement the expenses of their hobby. A garden is too small to support a cow—or in many cases even a goat. Sometimes chickens can compete, in a small garden, for the space required for vegetables and fruit. One or two stocks of bees take up very little room and, as the old saying goes 'The bee helps the garden. The garden helps the bee. Man reaps the benefit of both.'

Honeybees can cover a very large area to collect enough nectar to produce honey for us. In keeping bees are we correcting an imbalance mankind has created by the destruction of many beneficial insects by indiscriminate spraying? Perhaps so. Certainly there is a feeling of satisfaction in contributing to the ecology of the area where our bees are kept.

Contrary to popular belief the countryside is not necessarily the most profitable place to keep bees. Unless the beekeeper is fortunate enough to be near a large flowering crop, the countryside can be a desert for bees—it is a source of wonder that the bees manage to get a crop at all!

However, many beekeepers in towns record very high yields of surplus honey. When we consider the avenues of ornamental trees and shrubs, the gardens full of flowers, and the parks and gardens of local authorities which provide many square miles of forage for the bees, this surplus is hardly surprising.

Bees, on the whole, are very quiet and go about their business in an unobtrusive way. Many bees have been kept in suburban gardens for years without the neighbourhood being aware of their existence—some even being kept on the roof of a block of flats! But it must be said that, with the best management in the world, bees do swarm, and this, to the uninitiated, can be a little alarming. It is surprising how the odd pot of honey now and then helps neighbourly relationships.

Bees, unlike much other livestock, lend themselves to fitting in with the general household routine. They don't have to be attended to night and morning, and the beekeeper can go away on holiday without having to arrange for someone to come in and look after them—they will look after themselves. During the winter months the beekeeper has nothing to do for the bees, so the problem of going out in inclement weather to attend to 'the stock' does not arise.

There are as many ways of keeping bees as there are beekeepers. Each beekeeper develops a system that suits him and this variety is reflected in beekeeping literature. In order to avoid confusion I have confined myself to describing one basic hive, one system of keeping bees and one simple method of increasing the number of colonies. As you meet more beekeepers and read more books you will become aware of the great variety and interest in our craft.

Beekeepers are a friendly bunch of people who are always willing to help each other. Joining the local beekeepers' association puts a beekeeper in touch with many experienced people who will be willing to help newcomers get settled with their bees. The lectures, courses and demonstrations provided by these organisations are invaluable. The address of the secretary of your local beekeepers' association can be obtained from the British Beekeepers' Assn.

1 Bees

The honeybee has been known and exploited by man for many thousands of years.

Honeybees are social insects—the 'mother', adults and young all survive the winter together. To do so they must have a store of food in the form of honey. They sometimes store much more than they require and it is this surplus that the beekeepers take for themselves.

Honeybees have never been domesticated like cattle and horses. Man has provided boxes for them to live in but they are still wild creatures. The boxes, or hives, are only a convenience for the beekeeper to enable him to exploit the bee.

Of the four kinds of honeybee that exist in the world today the one that concerns us in Britain is the Western Honeybee. There are several forms of this bee. They are all very closely related but differ considerably in colour and slightly in wing-size and length of tongue. They all produce honey and if conditions are right they produce a surplus; which is why we are interested in them initially. Later, many beekeepers become interested in every aspect of the honeybee.

The honeybee, in many ways, resembles most other insects in that it has a head, a thorax (to which the wings and legs are attached) and an abdomen which is more than half the length of the bee and contains most of the digestive, respiratory and circulatory systems. Two, big, multi-lensed, compound eyes are on either side of the head. There are three, simple, much smaller eyes on the top of the head. Two long feelers or antennae are attached to the front of the face. With these the bee can sense taste, touch and smell.

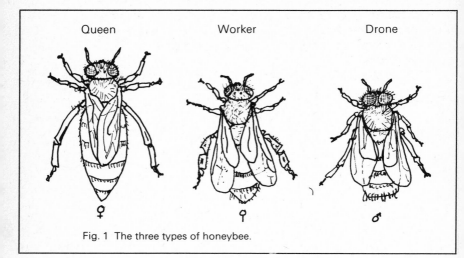

Queen   Worker   Drone

♀   ♀   ♂

Fig. 1 The three types of honeybee.

There are two pairs of wings, the front pair being larger than those at the back. The wings on each side are folded over one another when not in use but when spread they are joined to form one surface by hooks on the leading edge of the hind wing fitting into a groove on the trailing edge of the forewing. So the bees have the ability to 'unzip' their wings and fold them away when not in use!

There are three types of bee in the colony. The worker, the queen, and the drone. (Fig. 1.)

The worker

The worker bee is female by nature, but since she is not entire she cannot lay eggs except in very unusual circumstances. Much of her anatomy is adapted to fulfil functions unique to the worker bee. Her tongue is used for sucking up and ripening nectar; when not in use it is folded away. She has mandibles or jaws on each side of her tongue which are used for working wax. Her three pairs of legs have many special

16

features. The front legs each have a very small notch, lined with hairs, which is used for cleaning the antennae. The hind legs have brushes for cleaning pollen off the bee's body, and a 'basket' in which to carry the pollen. (Fig. 2.)

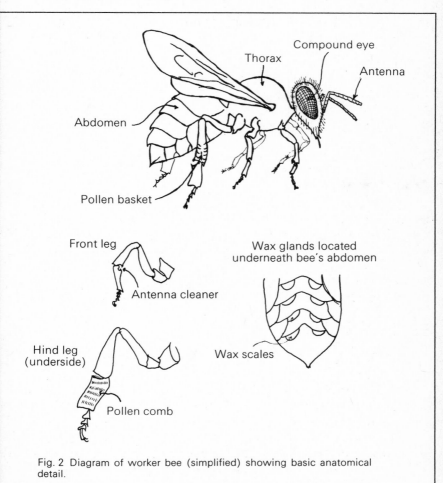

Fig. 2 Diagram of worker bee (simplified) showing basic anatomical detail.

The workers care for the eggs and larvae, build combs, feed and clean the queen, guard the hive, and search for and collect nectar and pollen from many different flowers. The life of worker bees can be very short during the height of the summer, only five weeks, as this is the time when they are doing most of their flying. But the workers that survive the winter may live for more than five months.

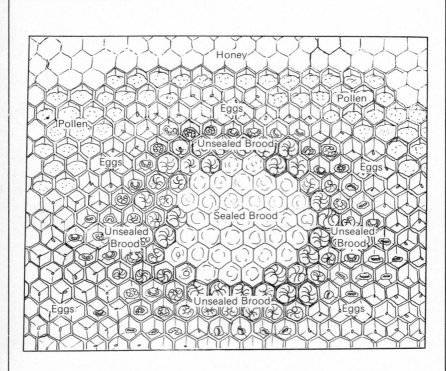

Fig. 3 Part of a brood comb showing honey, pollen, eggs and larvae in all stages.

Although they are the smallest of the types of bee in the colony the workers make up for this in numbers. As many as 98 per cent of the bees may be workers. It is the workers that sting but they only do this in defence of the colony.

During the early part of her life within the hive the worker fulfils many duties. The first three days are spent getting stronger and waiting for the glands within her body to develop. Meanwhile she works at cleaning out cells and getting them ready for the queen to lay in. From the third day to the sixth day she feeds older larvae (older than three days) with a mixture of honey and pollen. Day six sees the development of the glands in her head which provide the brood food or 'royal jelly' and her time is spent feeding the younger larvae (up to three days old). After this, her wax glands become active and up to the twentieth day of her life she may be engaged in wax making, processing nectar into honey, helping with the air-conditioning duties that keep the hive at an even temperature and humidity, and doing guard duty at the entrance, ready to eject any strangers. She does leave the hive during this time and from the seventh day onwards will leave for orientation flights to establish where the hive is in relation to its surroundings. After day twenty she starts to forage for nectar and pollen. All this is shown in Table 1. The sequence of events can be altered to suit changing conditions, and old foragers can feed larva and build combs should the need arise.

The queen
There is only one queen in a hive, unless the circumstances are unusual. She is bigger than the other bees. Her wings are slightly longer than those of the worker though they appear shorter because of her longer abdomen. She has a broader thorax and her

Table 1. 'Duties' of Worker Bee	
Days after bee emerges	*Duties*
1st to 3rd	Cleaning cells and helping to maintain temperature within the hive by 'covering' brood.
3rd to 6th	Feeding older larvae with honey and pollen.
6th to 15th	Feeding younger larvae with brood food from her glands.
10th to 20th	Processing nectar into honey. Wax making. Guarding the hive. Helping to maintain hive temperature.
After 20th	Foraging for nectar, pollen, propolis and water. This period at the height of summer may be as short as two or three weeks before the bee works herself to death. Conversely this period of her life in winter when she has no foraging to do may be extended from November to April.

The above table can only give an indication of the times the worker carries out these duties. The timing is flexible and, in the main, can be extended, contracted, or missed out all together, depending on the demands of the colony.

legs are longer and brighter in colour. She moves over the combs in a stately way and often appears much shinier than the other bees. She can live for more than three years, and her main function is to lay eggs. She is fed by the workers on food produced in special glands in their heads. At the height of summer the queen is able to lay up to 2,000 eggs a day. Usually she only flies from the colony in her very early life, as a virgin on her mating flight and when the colony swarms. She has a curved sting which she is very reluctant to use except on rival queens.

The drone

Drones are the males of the colony. A few of the numbers present may mate with a queen. They are present in the colony from about May until about the end of September. They are much larger than the worker and are often mistaken for the queen by new beekeepers when they first see them walking on the comb. This mistake is quickly noticed when it is seen there are ten or more on the same comb! They have a square end to their abdomen and have no sting. For a completely harmless creature they make a lot of noise; this is a low, loud drone—from which they get their name. They do not contribute to the day-to-day running of the colony as they have no equipment to do so. They can feed from the honey cells but prefer to be fed by the workers. Unlike the workers they are accepted in any hive but they usually stay in the hive where they were born.

The colony tolerates quite a large number of drones during the summer months and the workers seem to work enthusiastically when they are present. In times of dearth, however, the drones are the first to go. At the end of summer they are ejected from the hive and left to the mercy of the elements.

Cells

The combs within the frames in the hive are made up of wax cells. There are two main sizes of cell: worker cells—about five millimetres across, and drone cells—about seven millimetres across. These cells are six-sided with the base of the cells on one side of the frame fitting into the base of the cells on the other side (see Fig. 4). The different sizes are used for rearing different sorts of bee—drones from drone cells, workers from worker cells. The mouth of the cell is slightly higher than the base. Both types of cell are also used for storing honey.

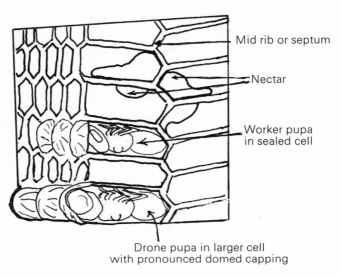

Mid rib or septum

Nectar

Worker pupa
in sealed cell

Drone pupa in larger cell
with pronounced domed capping

Fig. 4 Section through comb.

A queen cell, much larger than the worker and drone cells, is quite unlike them in structure. It is built up from a small cup of wax in which the queen lays an egg, and as the larva grows the workers extend the cell to hang down from the comb. It is often said to look rather like an acorn. (Fig. 5.)

Wax

The wax to make the cells is produced from wax glands on the worker bee. There are four pairs of these glands on the underside of the abdomen which exude flakes of wax (see Figure 2). The wax is chewed and softened by the bee and during this process other substances are mixed with it. The wax glands of the worker will secrete wax only when the bees cluster

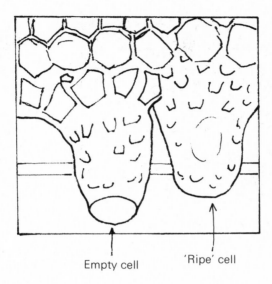

Empty cell   'Ripe' cell

Fig. 5 Queen cells.

together to raise the temperature. They also consume a lot of honey to create this heat. It has been estimated that the bees 'burn up' about two kilogrammes of honey to make half a kilogramme of wax. This makes beeswax valuable! Using beeswax foundation in the frames as a starting material for the bees saves a considerable amount of work, time, energy and wax. It also encourages the bees to build comb where the beekeeper wants it.

From egg to bee

The queen usually lays one egg in each cell, working from the centre of the frame outwards in a spiral: a fertile egg in a worker cell which will produce a worker; an infertile egg in a drone cell which will produce a drone; and a fertile egg in a queen cell producing a queen.

Life starts in the same way for all three types of bee. In each case the egg stage lasts for three days, the larva hatching on the third day. For the next three days the larva is fed on food from the glands situated at the head of the worker bee. This food is called 'royal jelly'. Worker and drone larvae are then fed on a mixture of pollen and honey for a further two days and the cells are capped over on the ninth day with a capping of wax.

If the larva is destined to become a queen it suffers no change of diet and is fed exclusively and liberally on royal jelly from the workers' glands until the cell is capped over also on the ninth day. After capping over, the three types of bee develop at different rates. Twenty-one days after the egg is laid the worker emerges; twenty-four days after the egg is laid the drone emerges; sixteen days after the egg is laid the queen emerges. It is during the period when the larva is sealed that it becomes a pupa, metamorphosis takes place, and the perfect insect emerges. (Fig. 6.)

Any worker larva that is not more than three days old can be changed into a queen if fed on the correct food throughout the larval stage. The worker bees will do this if for any reason the queen is lost, and enlarge the worker cell into a queen cell. As was said earlier the eggs laid in worker cells and queen cells are identical. It is how the workers feed the larva that determines whether the imago will be a queen or a worker. So, the queen could be said to be a product of nurture rather than nature since she is produced by feeding on royal jelly throughout the larval stage. Or, perhaps more accurately, all fertile eggs are potential queens, and workers are produced by denying them this special food after the first three days of the larval stage.

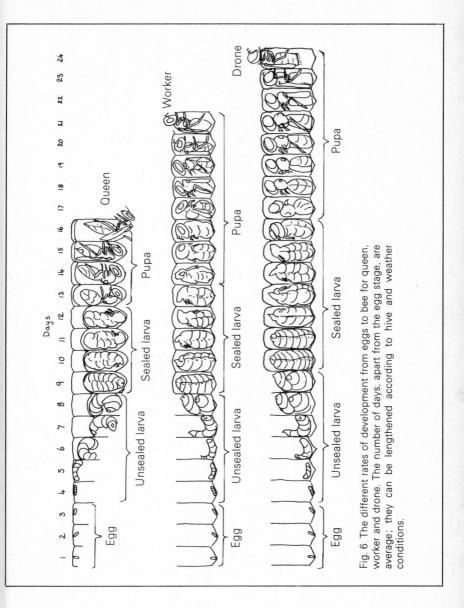

Fig. 6 The different rates of development from eggs to bee for queen, worker and drone. The number of days, apart from the egg stage, are average; they can be lengthened according to hive and weather conditions.

Mating

The queen mates on the wing with anything up to ten drones. The drones are not necessarily from her own hive. Some fairly recent research has shown that drones from a wide area may congregate in a special place to be available for the mating flight. During the mating flight the queen acquires sufficient sperm to last for the rest of her active egg-laying life. This sperm is stored in a special gland in her body. When the mating flight is over the queen will return to her hive to start egg laying. This she will do for the rest of her life. She will never mate again if her first mating flight is successful and she will now never leave the hive except when the colony swarms. The virgin queen is mature enough for mating a few days after emerging from her cell. The drone takes about ten days to mature and be capable of mating. The mating flight can only happen in fine sunny weather. If the mating flight is delayed too long by bad weather the queen will probably start to lay. Since she has no sperm in her sperm bank she can lay only infertile eggs—which will produce drones, and once she has started to lay she is incapable of mating.

The colony

By the height of summer the colony is at its largest, with the queen laying at her maximum and the number of bees in the hive being in the region of sixty thousand. As autumn approaches, the queen's egg-laying rate slows down, the drones are ejected from the hive and the bees go into their winter cluster. The queen lays very few eggs during the early part of winter and she may stop laying altogether for a while. During January and February life starts to quicken in the hive. The queen starts to lay more eggs—slowly at first and then in increasing numbers as the first months of the year (and the coldest months of winter) pass. As the younger bees replace the old, egg laying increases rapidly.

Swarming

It is when the colony has grown and the bees are crowded in the hive that swarming takes place. The causes of swarming are still not fully understood but certainly overcrowding is a dominant factor. The colony starts its preparation for swarming by producing drones and queens. When the queen cells are capped over, the swarm will emerge. The old queen, about half the workers and some of the drones will fly off. There may be as many as thirty thousand bees.

The swarm usually settles nearby and then after a time takes off again to a new site to settle permanently. Here the workers draw out new comb. To enable them to do this they will each have filled up their honey stomachs before they left the original colony and thus depleted much of any surplus honey that colony may have had. Not only this, but half the foraging bees will have left the colony at a time when there is most nectar available.

In the original colony one of the new queens will emerge and kill all the other queens in their cells. Alternatively she may leave the hive with a small swarm, or cast, leaving the next queen which emerges to take over the colony. However, one queen is eventually left to head the colony and the pattern of life gets back to normal.

The honeybees' harvest

When foraging among the flowers the bees are gathering two things: pollen and nectar. Nectar constitutes the carbohydrates of the bees' diet and pollen provides the protein. To attract insects, plants secrete nectar which is a watery substance containing sugars. Some plants secrete a more concentrated mixture than others and are more attractive to the bees. The bees suck up the liquid, store it in their honey stomachs and return to the hive with it. It is then passed on to the other bees who will convert it into honey.

From the stamen of the flowers the bees collect pollen. Different plants have different-coloured pollens which, when packed into the cells, make a most attractive, colourful pattern. The bees when foraging get covered with pollen—to the advantage of the plant, which becomes pollinated as the bee moves from flower to flower. The bees clean off the pollen with their legs and store it for transportation on the outside of their hind legs in special 'pollen baskets'. They sometimes make special journeys for the sole purpose of collecting pollen—returning home with full pollen baskets, looking rather like old gentlemen in plus-fours. Once in the hive the pollen is placed in the cells where the bees pack it very firmly by ramming it in, using their heads as rams. The pollen will be fed mostly to the larvae so it is stored close to the brood in the combs.

Bees and larvae can be fed on nectar as it comes into the hive. When there is more nectar than is required for immediate use it is converted into honey for use later. Extra pollen is stored for winter feeding and is preserved in the cells under a layer of honey.

Nectar, with its high water content, would ferment if stored in the cells without being 'ripened' by the bees. The younger bees who do this work take the nectar directly from the foragers as they return or from a cell where the nectar has been temporarily placed. Each of these young worker bees fills her honey stomach and finds a quiet place in the hive where the temperature is high. Here she exposes the nectar a small drop at a time on her tongue. Water is evaporated from the droplet which is then taken down into the honey stomach again. This process goes on and on until most of the water is evaporated and the nectar has become honey which is now a thick, viscous liquid. During this process the cane sugar in the nectar is inverted by a secretion from another of the bee's specialised glands. The honey is placed in the cells where the final 'ripening' takes place before the cells are capped over with wax. Having reached this stage, the honey will stay in good condition for a very long time.

The foraging bees collect another substance called propolis or bee glue. This sticky substance they usually find on plants where it is exuded from small cracks or breaks in the skin or bark. 'Sticky buds' in the spring are a very good source of supply. The bees carry it back to the hive in their pollen baskets. It is very difficult to remove and other bees have to help them. Propolis is used as a glue to fill up any small cracks or spaces in the hive—it helps to keep out the wind and rain and to stabilise any insecure parts. It is thought the bees also use it to mix with wax to make the combs stronger.

Although bees get a large amount of water in the nectar they gather this is not always sufficient or convenient for their needs. They need water in the spring to dilute the honey for feeding. Water is carried back to the hive in the same way as nectar. The colony also uses water to control the temperature in the hive when it is very hot. Water placed in the mouth of cells helps to cool the combs. By fanning their wings rapidly the bees are able to create a current of air through the hive to speed up this cooling process. The incubation of eggs and larvae also relies on a certain amount of humidity created by the presence of water.

As the foraging bees get more experienced they become more adventurous and may travel several kilometres from the hive in search of nectar. If one bee finds a rich source she is able to communicate this to the other bees in the hive by a series of 'dances' or movements on the face of the comb which indicate to the other bees the direction, distance and abundance of the source of nectar. This form of communication is also used when a swarm first settles, to indicate a dry, sheltered place to live in.

Winter survival

During the winter months the colony forms itself into a cluster. Its shape across and through the combs is rather like that of a rugby ball. (Fig. 7.)

The purpose of the cluster is to maintain a constant level of temperature and humidity over the brood area. The brood area is much reduced, as has already been noted, by the slowing down of the queen's egg-laying rate. However it must be remembered that the queen continues to lay a small quantity of eggs even in the depth of winter and the incubation temperature of the eggs and resulting brood is 32°C. It has been shown that the bees will maintain this temperature even though the temperature outside the cluster, but still within the hive, is 0°C and the temperature outside is −4°C or less. During these very cold temperatures the bees in the cluster are tightly packed together with very little air movement within. When the temperature goes up the cluster becomes loose with the bees spaced more widely apart, allowing a free flow of air up through the cluster. The bees do not remain stationary or inactive during this time. It is thought that they change places—those on the outside of the cluster moving to the inside and vice versa. When the bees are cold they become very slow and their metabolic rate slows down. There is therefore very little consumption of stores. Those bees in the centre of the cluster tending the small patches of

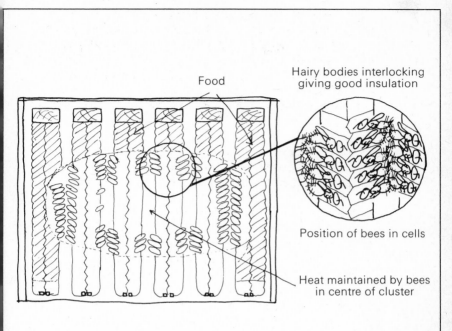

Food

Hairy bodies interlocking
giving good insulation

Position of bees in cells

Heat maintained by bees
in centre of cluster

Fig. 7 Diagram of section through frames in winter.

brood will be consuming stores, using up energy and
creating heat (see Figure 7).

As the stores are used up and the cells become
empty the cluster moves to cover them and give the
queen greater egg-laying space. The cluster expands
upwards and outwards. Figure 8 shows how the bees
use their winter stores and the space in the hive, and it
can be seen that the anxious time for the beekeeper is
late March and early April when the bees may well
have used up all their stores and are knocking on the
crown board for food!

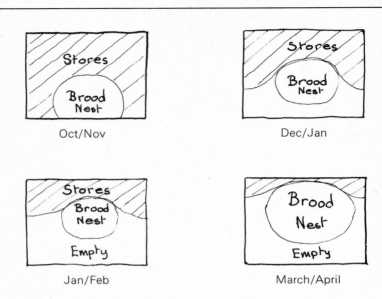

Oct/Nov

Dec/Jan

Jan/Feb

March/April

Fig. 8 Diagram showing possible size and position of brood nest and stores during winter months.

2 Equipment

Personal equipment

Some items of personal beekeeping equipment are essential. Certainly a well-fitting bee-veil to protect the face and neck from stings is an item that no beekeeper can afford to be without. It must do its job effectively without being too cumbersome or heavy. The all-in-one hat and veil is very good (see Figure 9(a)) but any veil that is held away from the face and allows the beekeeper clear vision is adequate. Elastic tapes at the bottom of the veil will fit it snugly to the shoulders and chest to prevent the bees getting underneath.

An overall of some sort is useful. A white boiler suit is ideal since it covers the whole body—particularly if there are no gaps that the bees might find. Pockets on the outside of the garment are most useful for holding odds and ends like matches; and it is surprising how often one wants to wipe one's nose when a handkerchief is tucked away in an inside pocket under the boiler suit! Tucking the bottom of the legs inside wellington boots or tying them prevents the odd bee getting in. When working with the hives beekeepers tend to get a little grubby so the boiler suit also protects clothes. Bees are reputed to dislike the colour blue so it might be as well to avoid this colour in an overall intended for use when working with the bees. Certainly woolly clothing or cloths, particularly if brown in colour, tend to infuriate the bees.

Gloves are advisable if the intending beekeeper is at all nervous. Once confidence has been gained and one has become more experienced the gloves may be discarded and stored away for the odd occasion when they might be needed. The type supplied by the manufacturers have useful long gauntlets attached to cover the gap between glove and sleeve. Many beekeepers who do not wear gloves still wear gauntlets to prevent the bees crawling up their sleeves. Rubber kitchen gloves have proved to be useful, giving more 'feel' than leather gloves and giving a fair degree of protection. It is worth saying here that if gloves get stung during the time you are looking at your bees it is a good idea to wash them before you go to the bees again. The smell of venom stays on the glove and this tends to excite the bees to sting next time they are visited.

A hive tool is specially designed for prising parts of the hive apart (see Figure 9(b)). It fulfils many functions. All types of hive tool have a flat sharpened blade for use as a scraper and some of the more recent ones have a 'tail' that is useful for prising up the frames.

The smoker (see Figure 9(c)) is used for subduing or directing the bees while looking through the hive. When working through a colony of bees few operations are possible without a readily available supply of smoke from a good smoker. Most smokers are made of tin, some of copper or stainless steel. These latter two will obviously last much longer than the tin variety. A good smoker with sturdy bellows and a reasonably-sized firebox is less likely to go out in the middle of an operation. Rolls of corrugated cardboard are a popular form of fuel but this does tend to burn away rather quickly when the bellows are not in active use. There are several alternative fuels if one has access to them. Dry hessian sacking, particularly if it is rotten, is a slow-burning fuel. Care must be taken that the sack has not contained anything toxic. Old *cotton* rags and well-rotted wood also make excellent fuels.

(a) Combined bee-hat and veil

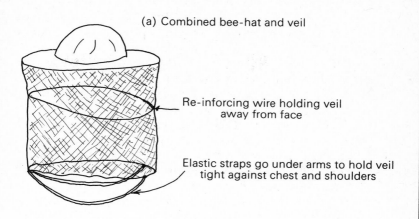

Re-inforcing wire holding veil
away from face

Elastic straps go under arms to hold veil
tight against chest and shoulders

(b) Hive tool and frame lifter

(c) Smoker

Bent nose nozzle

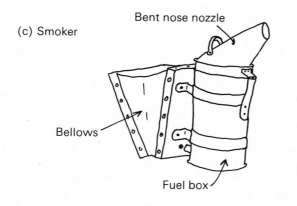

Bellows

Fuel box

Fig. 9 Personal equipment.

The hive

In the past a popular hive was the W.B.C. This is the hive that many people picture when thinking of bees and hives. It is a double-walled hive, the inner boxes containing the frames and bees, the outer parts, called lifts, protecting the inner boxes. It can be seen that all the outer parts have to be removed to get to the boxes that contain the bees. It is now very much out of date, although the equipment manufacturers will still supply it if asked. It has a plethora of pieces that seem to be designed to trip up the beekeeper, no matter where they are stacked, when looking through the hive at the bees. It is mentioned here because many intending beekeepers are given one as a kindly gesture 'to get them started'.

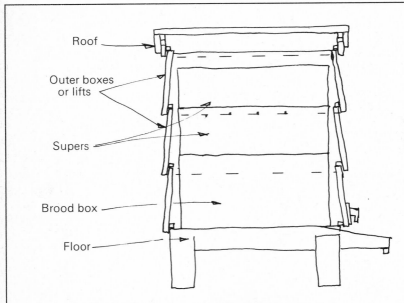

Fig. 10 W.B.C. hive (one side removed to show interior).

Any second-hand hive is suspect and should be thoroughly scorched on the inside with a blow lamp to kill off any spores or bacteria there may be. Certainly no colony of bees should be introduced to second-hand frames and comb unless one is very sure of the origin and that they are above suspicion. The only frames that really come into this category are the beekeepers' own that are known to come from healthy stock. All other sorts of second-hand brood frames should be put on the bonfire!

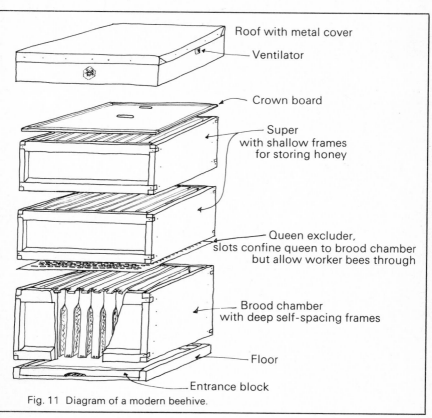

Roof with metal cover

Ventilator

Crown board

Super
with shallow frames
for storing honey

Queen excluder,
slots confine queen to brood chamber
but allow worker bees through

Brood chamber
with deep self-spacing frames

Floor

Entrance block

Fig. 11 Diagram of a modern beehive.

The National Hive is probably the most popular hive nowadays. It is a single-walled hive with its size based on the frames that are used in the W.B.C. This size of frame is now British Standard. Hives with a much more capacious brood chamber are used a lot but mainly by commercial and semi-commercial beekeepers. The parts of these commercial hives do tend to get rather heavy when fully of honey which makes them difficult to lift. Figure 11 shows the parts of the National Hive. When starting beekeeping it may be that not all these parts are necessary. The floor, brood chamber, crown board and roof would be sufficient to hive a small colony, or nucleus, of bees. The other parts of the hive (the queen excluder and supers) can be added as the bees require them.

The frames that fit in the hive have many different designs. The self-spacing frame has proved to be easy to use in the brood chamber and less of a 'fiddle' than frames that require separate spacers.

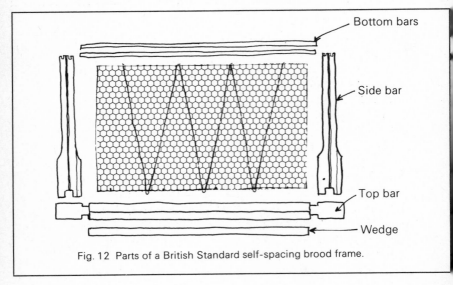

Fig. 12 Parts of a British Standard self-spacing brood frame.

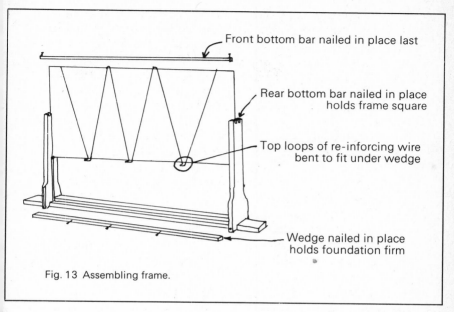

Front bottom bar nailed in place last

Rear bottom bar nailed in place
holds frame square

Top loops of re-inforcing wire
bent to fit under wedge

Wedge nailed in place
holds foundation firm

Fig. 13 Assembling frame.

Frames already fitted with sheets of wax foundation can be bought from the manufacturers but it is much cheaper to buy the frames in parts and put them together oneself. This is a relatively simple and satisfying activity (see Figure 13).

As with frames, hives can be 'made up' from parts accurately machined and ready to put together. Hives ready for making up are described in the makers' catalogues as 'in the flat'.

Bee space and hive construction

Before discussing hives and their construction further, a word must be said about bee space. Bee space is roughly 8 mm. Below 6 mm the bees will fill the gap with propolis; above 9 mm the bees will fill the gap with brace comb. So it will be seen that in order to be able to remove the frames from the hive there must be a space of approximately 8 mm between the frames and the walls of the hive. This also applies to the space between the top of the frames of one box and the bottom of the frames of the box above or anything placed between, e.g. the queen excluders and clearer boards. (Fig. 14.)

In the construction of a hive it is important to maintain this bee space and this is one of the reasons why hives are made of Western red cedar, a wood that has very little expansion and contraction. It also has the advantages of needing no preservative and being light. Many hobbyist beekeepers make their own hives of other timbers quite successfully but they do need painting regularly with a preservative that will allow the wood to 'breathe' and great care must be

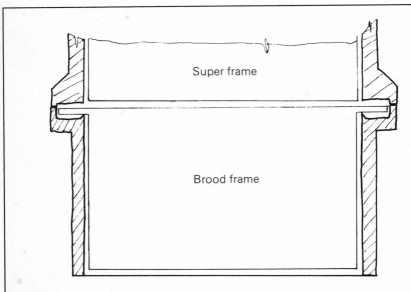

Fig. 14 Section through hive showing bee space round frame and between boxes.

taken to ensure that the hives are not painted with any substance that contains insecticide or insect repellant as this can have disastrous effects on bees. During the past few years experiments have been made, with varying degrees of success, with plastics, such as polythene and polyurethane. It is hoped that Appendix A will be of use to those who want to put a hive together themselves and that the dimensions will help those who may want to make their own.

Having established the first hive in the apiary it is advisable to always stick to the same design for the second and subsequent hives. It is time-consuming and infuriating for the beekeeper and the bees when parts of hives in the apiary are not interchangeable.

3 Starting Beekeeping

With beekeeping, as with many other profitable hobbies, there is an initial outlay. The hives, bees and other equipment need to be bought; but, having got established, the year-to-year running costs are reduced to those of renewing frames and wax, purchasing honey jars and buying sugar for feeding. The production of honey for sale should cover the running costs with, perhaps, a little over. Certainly the household should never go short of honey if the bees produce an average of 14 kg of honey in a year.

The apiary needs little space and the bees need regular attention only during the summer months. The time spent with the bees declines as experience is acquired and although initially an hour a week may be needed to inspect each colony, within a few months of getting the bees this time is reduced considerably. There are times of the year, such as harvest time, when a day or two will need to be set aside for the extraction and bottling of honey. A discipline of regular inspections is required of the beekeeper during the summer months but the bees can fit in with very little interruption of the normal household routine and if one is on a holding with other livestock, again bees can fit into a horticultural or agricultural pattern very easily. After keeping bees for a little while one gains confidence and courage; patience and a keen sense of observation follow.

Acquiring the bees

Initially there are three possible ways of getting bees: a swarm, package bees, and a nucleus. It might seem to be best to buy a strong colony to start with in the hope of seeing a return in the form of a honey crop in the first year. But a really strong colony of bees does have problems of management that a complete beginner to beekeeping may not be able to cope with. It is probably best, therefore, to start with a small colony of bees that will grow in strength in the first year as the new beekeeper grows in experience.

Swarms

Getting a swarm is probably not the best way to start. Many of the disadvantages are dealt with in detail later in the book. Swarms are sometimes available at the beginning of the year but the supply cannot be relied upon.

Package bees

Package bees from America, New Zealand, France and other countries are imported from time to time by the main appliance manufacturers. A package usually consists of about 2.5 kg of bees with a queen in a separate queen cage. The box they come in has wire gauze sides to give the bees plenty of ventilation. The box may also contain a small tin of sugar syrup which provides the bees with food while they are in transit. They are best hived on drawn comb, but this a beginner is unlikely to have, so they must be hived on foundation. Hiving instructions are sent with the packages but the process is a little detailed and not recommended for a novice unless expert help is to hand. The bees need careful management and a lot of feeding in the early stages of their development as a colony.

Nucleus

A nucleus of bees (that is, bees as a complete yet small colony on 4, 6, or 8 frames) is a self-sufficient, working unit that is ideal for the novice beekeeper to start with. It must be emphasised that the bees will need feeding until they have expanded sufficiently and become strong enough in numbers to look after themselves. A nucleus consists of frames of comb with sufficient bees to cover all surfaces, except perhaps the outer surfaces of the end combs; the outer frames should be full of stores in the form of honey and pollen, the inner frames being two thirds full of brood in all stages from eggs to capped larvae; the whole being accompanied by a young, mated, laying queen who will have free access to the frames for egg laying. All this is contained in a travelling box, which is a lightweight, small hive with plenty of ventilation, its lid screwed down and the entrance secured by perforated zinc.

Any nucleus of bees offered cheap would probably fail to meet the above standard and would be a potentially weak colony. All the main, reputable dealers supply nuclei of bees to a British Standard Specification similar to that described above.

Before the nucleus of bees arrives it is as well to be prepared with a hive into which the bees are to be transferred, extra frames and foundation, personal beekeeping equipment and tools, and a prepared apiary site. If the nucleus arrives and cannot be dealt with straight away the bees should be placed in a cool, shady spot until they can be transferred to their hive. If there is going to be some longer delay before transfer, the travelling box can be placed on the exact spot where the hive is to stand and the entrance to the box opened to allow the bees to fly. They can be left like this overnight or longer if necessary. Before transferring the bees into the hive puff a little smoke in at the entrance and through the ventilating screens of the travelling box. Move the box to one side and set up the hive on the site the travelling box occupied. Unscrew the top of the travelling box and take off the lid. Before placing the lid on the ground make sure the queen is not on the underside of it. Puff a little smoke over the top of the frames, then transfer them one at a time into the hive in exactly the same order and position as they occupied in the travelling box. You may see the queen as the combs are transferred, but do not spend time looking for her at this stage. When all the frames are in the hive the travelling box should be held upside down over the hive and the remaining bees shaken out. Make sure the queen is not in the box before doing so. If she is, she needs coaxing onto the frames in the hive. When the frames have been transferred they need to be flanked by frames of foundation and all the frames closed up to one side of the box leaving a space of about 6 mm between the wall of the hive and the first frame. The space in the hive the other side of the frames should be blanked off with a dummy board. The entrance to the hive needs to be closed down to a small gap of about 25 mm. The bees will need feeding. They have a lot of work to do to build up into a strong colony and the feeding needs to continue until all the foundation is drawn out.

Feeders

Perhaps the simplest form of feeder is the contact feeder. The feeding area of the container comes into direct contact with the colony of bees so that they do not have to break cluster or travel far from the combs. The bees have access to the syrup through small holes punched in the lid of an otherwise airtight container which is placed upside down over the feed hole in the crown board (see Figure 15(a)).

Small feeders can be made from empty instant coffee jars. The cardboard wad needs to be removed and holes punched in the lid from the outside. This ensures that the jagged edges of the hole are on the inside. The holes can be made by driving a small nail into the metal just sufficiently for the point to break

45

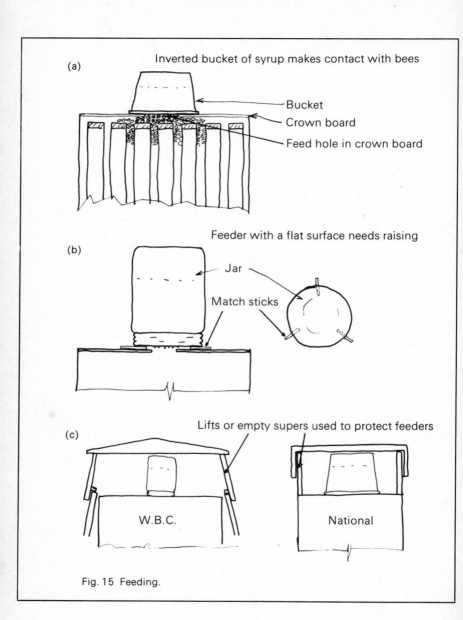

(a) Inverted bucket of syrup makes contact with bees

— Bucket
— Crown board
— Feed hole in crown board

(b) Feeder with a flat surface needs raising

Jar

Match sticks

(c) Lifts or empty supers used to protect feeders

W.B.C.

National

Fig. 15 Feeding.

through. If the shaft of the nail is driven through the hole will probably be too large and the container will leak.

Large feeders can be made from plastic buckets that have an airtight lid. Holes can be made in the lid with a large safety pin. About forty holes should be sufficient. If the buckets or other containers are used for mixing the sugar syrup in, a wipe with a damp cloth to remove any grains of sugar from the rim of the container and the lip of the lid will help in keeping the container airtight.

Glass and plastic containers seem to have an advantage over tin inasmuch as they are easier to clean and sterilise and the level of the syrup can be seen without removing them from the hive.

The lids of some coffee jars and some plastic containers may be 'flush'. If matchsticks are placed under the container when they are put on the hive this will give the bees a little headroom (see Figure 15(b)). An empty super can be placed on the crown board to protect the feeder from wind, rain and the attentions of marauding wasps! (See Figure 15(c).)

4 Management

Siting

Placing the hives in a spot that is dry, airy, sunny but sheltered from the winds, with room to increase the number of hives, is the first step towards good management. If the site is to be on a large plot of land there may be plenty of choice. In a garden the choice may be restricted and the environs created. If there is a spot away from the house (and other people's houses) that is on firm ground, sheltered from the prevailing winds by trees or hedges without overhanging the hives then this is a good basis for an apiary site. Surrounding the area with a hedge or fencing high enough to elevate the bees' line of flight above neighbours and passers-by is essential in a cramped area. Many suburban beekeepers grow their runner beans in front of the hives so that when they are working in the garden they are not in the bees' flight line. The plot for the apiary should be large enough for an increase in the number of colonies and leave enough room for the beekeeper to work the hives. Figures 16 and 17 give an idea of the sort of layout that is suitable.

The hives should be set on firm stands to raise them above the ground. This gives a good flow of air all round the hive and raises the brood chamber to a height that is more easily workable. It is preferable for the entrances of the hive to have a southerly aspect but this is not essential. The surroundings should be kept free from tall grass and weeds, as this tends to hinder the movements of the beekeeper. A hard standing of flags or concrete is ideal but not always practicable. Figure 18 shows a simple form of hive stand that is easy to construct and has proved useful. Though it is

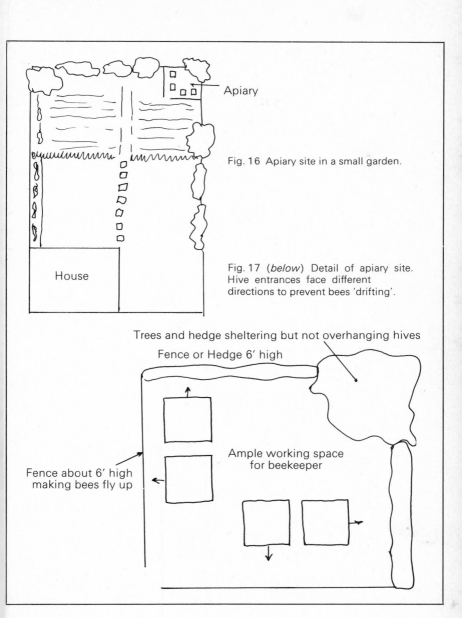

Apiary

Fig. 16 Apiary site in a small garden.

House

Fig. 17 (*below*) Detail of apiary site. Hive entrances face different directions to prevent bees 'drifting'.

Trees and hedge sheltering but not overhanging hives

Fence or Hedge 6' high

Ample working space for beekeeper

Fence about 6' high making bees fly up

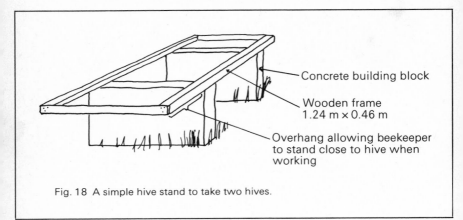

Fig. 18 A simple hive stand to take two hives.

Labels in figure:
- Concrete building block
- Wooden frame 1.24 m × 0.46 m
- Overhang allowing beekeeper to stand close to hive when working

advisable to start with one or two small colonies, these will increase as the years go by and the sort of site described will accommodate this increase within its confined area.

Inspection

Having a colony of bees is rather like any other addition to the family. Its presence is suddenly there, unpredictable and strange, and one is curious to know what they are doing in that box. The first few inspections are motivated by this curiosity and the beginner is as confused, if not more so, after as before! It is a great help to have a clear objective before inspecting the colony and not to allow oneself to be deflected from this objective. When beekeepers inspect their colonies they are looking for three main things: the presence of the queen, signs of swarming, and the presence of disease. It is always a joy, but not a necessity, to see the queen on routine inspections. As long as there are eggs and capped worker brood in a regular pattern (see Figure 3) she is there and laying. The presence of queen cells is a sign that the bees are preparing to swarm, and these cells must be dealt with. This is described in detail later in the chapter. The health of the brood and bees is noted (see Chapter 7). It is a great temptation at first to be over-enthusiastic about looking into the hives. It is as well not to be pulling them about too often as it takes the bees a little while to put things right after each inspection and they need time to settle to a regular pattern of development. After a time a system is developed for inspecting the colonies with the minimum amount of disturbance to the bees. Such a system is developed by all beekeepers to suit them-selves and becomes individual to them. Once you have found a system that suits you, stick to it. Read and listen to other people's ideas and if they seem sound adapt them to suit you.

Building up the colony

Starting with a small colony of bees in the spring is ideal. During the first season the colony will grow from a nucleus to be large enough to fill a brood chamber and the beekeepers can start with a small manageable colony and grow in confidence and competence with it. In the first season of such a colony the first aim is to get it built up in size and stores to 'go down' strong in the winter. During some recent seasons some very small colonies of this type have not only done that but also stored some surplus of honey for the beekeeper as well. A nucleus colony of four frames has a lot of work to do building out all the frames of the brood chamber from wax foundation, so the bees at this stage will need feeding. The contact feeder (see Figure 15) is very good. During the fortnight or so after feeding the bees will build up wax in the brood chamber and will be increasing in numbers to cover the frames. The bees need to be examined every seven days or so and frames of foundation added as they need them. More frequent inspections are unnecessary. The bees need a settled period to work. Only give extra frames one or two at a time. The bees will work the last frame in the group more easily if it is flanked by a dummy board, which is the size of an ordinary frame but made of solid wood (see Figure 24). When all the frames are nearly built out the bees may be reluctant to work on the face of the comb next to the side of the brood chamber. If these frames are turned round so the inner, built-up side, is outside and the outer, unbuilt side is inside the bees will then work on it. The frames can, if necessary, be swapped for the penultimate frames. Feed all the time.

Putting on the first super

When the bees are crowding on the penultimate frames and are beginning to work the last frames in the brood chamber it is time they had more room. A queen excluder is placed on the brood chamber to confine the queen there. A super with frames is placed on top, then the crown board and the feeder replaced. In the first season the frames in the super will have foundation that has not been built up. The frames in a super are usually on wider spacing to make the honeycomb wider than the frame, which is helpful when the time comes for extracting. However, when the frames are first put into the super they will need to be on narrow spacing to encourage the bees to work the wax in the frames. Both spacings can be achieved using a wide spacer (see Figure 19). Once the bees have started to build out the wax in the super the frames can be put in the wide spacing position and the feeder removed.

Young queens in their first year do not often swarm so there may be no swarm management in the first season. It may be that when autumn arrives there is a

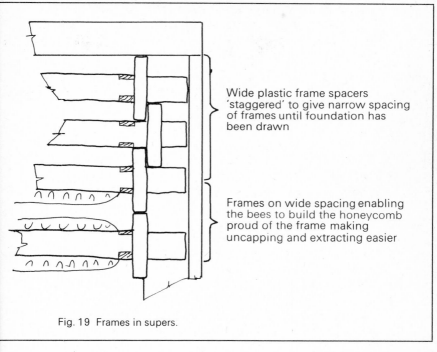

Wide plastic frame spacers 'staggered' to give narrow spacing of frames until foundation has been drawn

Frames on wide spacing enabling the bees to build the honeycomb proud of the frame making uncapping and extracting easier

Fig. 19 Frames in supers.

surplus of honey for the beekeeper who, having taken the honey off, will feed the colony well so that the bees face the winter months with plenty of stores.

The season's work

In March the beekeeper begins to think of the condition of the bees. By 'hefting' the hive—gently lifting the hive at the back—it is easy to determine whether the hive is heavy or light and gain an indication of the amount of stores the bees still have. If the bees are going to die of starvation in the winter it is during the months of March and April that they are most likely to succumb since the increase in brood is making more and more demands on the dwindling supplies. If the hive feels light the bees need feeding. As the temperature during the day increases and the daylight hours get longer the bees will be able to forage for the pollen they need.

As the warmer days arrive in late March and early April when the temperature gets up to and above 16°C—as it can in many parts of the country, except the far north, at this time of the year—the time comes for the first inspection. Four important things need doing. (1) Change or clean the floor board. If there is a spare floor to hand, the floors can be exchanged and the floor that has been on all winter can be cleaned later. It only takes a few moments to scrape off the detritus and debris with the hive tool and get the floor clean. (2) Inspect the frames for the queen (or the eggs she has laid) to establish the colony is queen-right. (3) Look for signs of disease. (4) Check the bees have plenty of stores. As soon as these things have been established close down the hive again, it is not necessary to go through all the frames at this stage. This inspection will also give an idea of how the bees are 'building up' in strength of numbers.

Control of swarming

The first weeks of May see the first of the regular inspections. From now on the presence of drones and the construction of queen cells will indicate the start of the swarming season. Swarming is the only way the honeybee colony can reproduce itself—it is a natural function. Beekeepers like to prevent swarming because, as we have seen, the bees take quite a bit of honey with them when they leave. Some beekeepers speak of swarming as if it were a disease and will not admit to it happening in their colonies! However, May is the time to look for signs. It is also a time to keep an eye on the space available for the bees. When the bees are crowding on the outside of the penultimate frames it is time to super. Scrape the tops of the frames in the brood chamber free from wax and propolis with the hive tool to preserve the bee space and allow the queen excluder to fit properly. There may be no surplus nectar coming into the hive at this time, it all being used for brood rearing, but the bees need the space. Overcrowding in the brood chamber may induce swarming.

Looking for queen cells

Many people run a 'double brood' or 'brood and a half' system. In the double-brood system the queen is given the run of two brood chambers, one on top of the other. In the brood-and-a-half system she is given the run of a brood chamber and a super. Management is the same for both. This system allows for a large brood area. During routine inspections for queen cells the brood boxes are opened where they join and the top box lifted back (see Figure 20(a)). If there are queen cells they will almost certainly be attached to the bottom of the frames in the top box. If there are no queen cells the boxes are placed back together with minimal disturbance to the bees. If, however, there are queen cells present all the frames in both boxes must be inspected. With a single brood chamber system, taking out and inspecting one frame from the middle of the brood nest for queen cells serves the same purpose with little disturbance to the brood area and if queen cells are present there is only one box to go through. Neither of these methods are fool-proof in detecting queen cells in a colony but they are good working methods with a high success rate.

Unless an increase in the number of the colonies is wanted, the queen cells and their occupants must be destroyed when they are discovered, having first made sure the queen is still in the colony. Having discovered the beginnings of queen cells in the colony

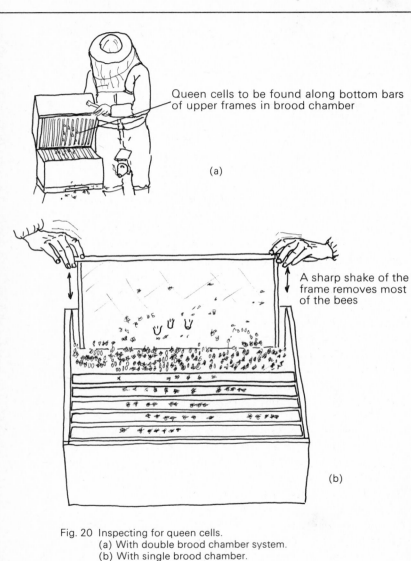

Queen cells to be found along bottom bars of upper frames in brood chamber

(a)

A sharp shake of the frame removes most of the bees

(b)

Fig. 20 Inspecting for queen cells.
(a) With double brood chamber system.
(b) With single brood chamber.

every frame in the brood chamber needs to be inspected carefully. To do this properly the bees must be removed as no queen cell must be missed. Removing the bees can be easily achieved by giving the frame a sharp shake over the brood chamber (see Figure 20(b)) and most of the bees will be dislodged and fall back into the brood chamber. The frame can then be studied thoroughly for queen cells. Care must be taken not to shake off the queen if possible. If she is seen she can be picked off the comb and allowed to run down on the frames already inspected. The brood frames are shaken over the brood chamber because of the possibility of not finding the queen! Some beekeepers mark their queens with a dot of special, bright-coloured paint on the back of the thorax to make it easier to see her in the mêlée of bees—it is advisable to see an experienced beekeeper mark queens before attempting it oneself. The colony needs to be looked at again in nine days' time to see if they have built any more queen cells since the queen cells are capped on the ninth day and this is the day the swarm will emerge. Many beekeepers find nine days an awkward number and look at their colonies on a seven-day cycle which fits in nicely with weekends.

Increasing the number of colonies

If the number of colonies is to be increased a good opportunity for doing so is presented when queen cells appear. The bees are wanting to increase themselves and are expecting to swarm. The bee-keeper merely speeds up the process. This method of increase is called artificial swarming. Figure 21 gives a diagrammatic layout of the process. For this operation a spare floor, brood chamber, crown board and roof are needed. After smoking the bees take any supers off the hive. Remove the queen excluder. Go through the colony and find the queen. Place her and the frame she is on, with its attendant bees, in the new brood chamber flanked by frames of foundation to fill the box. Place this new box on the original floor, so that the queen stays on her own site. The queen excluder, supers and roof are replaced. Put the old brood chamber with the queen cells and bees with new floor, crown board and roof on a new site about five metres away, thus creating a new colony. The entrance of the new colony is reduced to give the bees a better chance to defend themselves against robbing. The older, foraging bees, will return to the old site and continue working normally. This brood chamber then will have the appearance of having swarmed and the construction of queen cells will cease. The new colony, on the new site, with a frame of foundation to replace the one taken with the queen, will now have all young bees that will be able to provide the queen cells with a rich supply of brood food. This new colony needs to be left severely alone for at least three weeks. This will give the queen time to emerge, mate, and settle to a normal egg-laying routine before inspection. Young queens are notoriously fickle until they have settled into this steady egg-laying routine. When trying this system for the first time it may be as well to leave all the queen cells in the 'new' colony and let the first virgin queen to emerge sort out the others. There is a chance, of course, that she may leave the hive with a swarm soon after she emerges from her cell. This can be safeguarded against by making sure that there is only one uncapped queen cell in the new colony—uncapped because it will be seen that the cell has an occupant alive. If a capped queen cell is left there is no knowing whether the occupant is alive—or there at all. Care must be taken when handling the frames with queen cells not to knock or jar them as a sharp blow can dislodge the larva from its bed of 'royal jelly'.

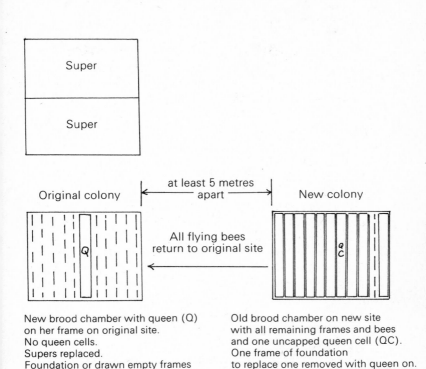

Fig. 21 Increasing the number of colonies by artificial swarm method.

At a later date, with more experience and equipment, there is an opportunity here during this time to make up two 5-frame nuclei. The ten frames in the brood chamber can be put into two five-frame boxes. Make sure that both lots have queen cells. If the entrances are tightly packed with grass, by the time it has wilted and the bees released themselves many of the older bees will stay with these small colonies; otherwise these small units would be depleted of too many bees, making survival difficult. The original colony will still have one frame with the queen, plus all the supers. The brood chamber will, of course, have to be filled up with drawn frames or frames of foundation.

This whole process of artificial swarming may be done even if there are no queen cells present as the bees will bring on some of the eggs, or more probably the larvae, as queens when they find they are queenless. It must be said, however, that the subsequent queens will not be as good as those brought on by the bees through a natural process rather than by force of circumstances. The latter will be emergency queens raised from larvae that were intended to be workers.

In the event that no extra colonies are required, removing the queen cells and giving the bees room may be sufficient to make the bees give up the attempt to swarm and they may not start any more queen cells.

However, despite these methods to prevent them swarming the bees may insist on doing so. They can only be restrained by the nine-day routine inspection and removal of queen cells as mentioned earlier. If on the third inspection the bees still insist on making queen cells they will swarm prior to the queen cells being capped, probably as soon as the new queen cells have eggs in, so the swarm will have gone before nine days are up. Making an artificial swarm, as described above, at the time of the third inspection with successive queen-cell building, may well prevent them swarming. Then at the end of the season the queen can be killed and the colony united with the new colony that has developed from the artificial swarm. An old, failing queen would then have been replaced by a young queen who will be less likely to swarm in her first season. Some colonies of bees seem to be more likely to swarm than others so it would be wise to increase the number of colonies from those that are less inclined to swarm and use the queens raised from these colonies to replace the queens in colonies that are more inclined to swarm.

This then is the main summer work through the months of May, June and July: giving the bees plenty of super space, preventing swarming, and increasing the number of colonies if so desired.

Uniting

Uniting colonies, when queens are lost, can be done at any time during the summer months. Uniting colonies when replacing queens is probably best done at the end of the season after the honey has been removed and before feeding begins. Always put the queenless colony on top of the queen-right colony when uniting. Put a queen excluder on the bottom, queen-right, colony. Place a single layer of news-paper, without any holes in it, to completely cover the queen excluder. Prick the newspaper with a pin. The holes in the newspaper must only be pin holes. Place the queenless brood chamber on the newspaper (see Figure 22). Put the crown board and roof in place as usual. The bees will chew their way through the newspaper to unite. The process is slow enough for the bees to absorb each other's colony smell and get used to each other and become one colony. If the process is too fast the bees will fight in defence of their respective colonies. The queen excluder will prevent the queen getting up and laying in the top chamber. After a few days the remains of the newspaper can be removed. Any brood that is in the top box will emerge and the young bees will go down into the bottom chamber. When all the brood has emerged the top chamber can be removed and the bees shaken off the

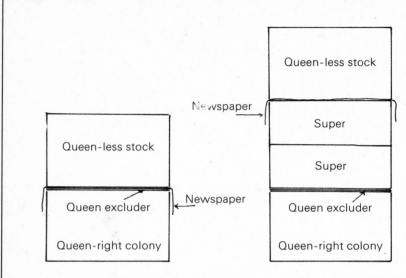

Fig. 22 Uniting queenless stock to queen-right colony by newspaper method. Queenless stock always goes above queen-right colony.

frames into the lower chamber. The top chamber and its frames, probably with some sealed stores, can be stored away ready for use in the spring to make up nuclei or to give to weak colonies. The queen excluder can be removed from the hive and the colony can now be fed at the same time as the other colonies in the apiary.

The end of the season

In August the evenings are beginning to draw in. The subsequent shortening of daylight hours and the drop in temperature changes the tempo within the hive. Swarming is known in August but most colonies have slowed down. The queen is now laying less although there is a spurt in her egg-laying activity during

September to provide over-wintering bees. So late in August and early September may well be harvest time for the beekeeper. Some areas have a late flow of nectar at this time and bees that are kept near heather may get a nectar flow from that plant during September and early October and the beekeeper may be harvesting at the end of that month. After the honey harvest, which is dealt with in the chapter on honey production, the bees need to be fed. The ability of the colony to produce a good harvest of honey in the next season depends on the ability to survive the winter and grow in strength in the spring. Plenty of sugar syrup fed in the autumn will help to achieve this. Feeding should take place soon after the honey harvest and be finished by late September. At least 15 litres of sugar syrup should be fed if the bees will take it. The sugar syrup should be mixed to the strength of about 2 kg of sugar to 1 litre of water. This should give a good thick syrup that the bees can utilise without too much reduction of the water content. A strong colony will need about 30 kg of stores in the combs to last the winter and be of use for feeding during the early spring.

At the end of the year, as the days get colder, mice seek a place to spend the winter. Hives make ideal homes and the beekeeper must take precautions against mice entering the hive by placing a mouse-guard over the entrance. These should have holes small enough to keep out the mice but large enough to allow free passage of the bees. Strips of metal, fastened securely across the entrance, with holes 5 mm in diameter serve the purpose very well and can be made from strips of perforated zinc. After the feeder has been removed the roof needs inspecting to make sure it is watertight. The ventilators in the roof need to be clear since for good wintering adequate ventilation for the colony is very important. The covers over the holes in the crown board need to be opened to the width of a matchstick (see Figure 23). At this time of the year the bees will ignore this space which assists in the free flow of air through the winter cluster of bees. Good ventilation prevents condensation within the hive.

During the cold winter months from November through into March the bees will not normally require any attention. The bees will cluster tightly during the cold and only break from the cluster on mild sunny days to make cleansing flights. When spring comes round, pollen and nectar become abundant, and the beekeeper's year starts all over again.

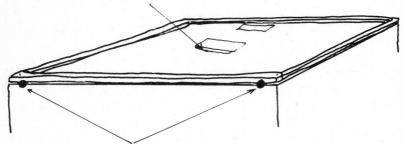

Strip, the thickness of match-stick, left uncovered in feed-hole

Alternative method: felt nails placed under edge of crown board

Fig. 23 Ventilation for winter. Time: end of October/beginning of November when bees will have stopped collecting propolis.

5 Handling the Colony

When thinking about handling a colony of bees it is worth remembering their likes and dislikes. Much of what we do and how we do it is based on the bees' behaviour. The things that keep bees contented are the things that add to the well-being of the colony: plenty of nectar coming in; an open aspect in front of the hive; lots of stores; normal brood and a mated laying queen; access to honey cells and warm, still weather. They do not like smoke, things blocking the entrance to the hive, very windy weather. They certainly do not like thundery weather. They do not like being disturbed when it is cold. Bees usually fly from the hive when the temperature gets above 10°C and it is advisable not to look at the bees unless the temperature is above 15°C or 16°C since the loss of heat when opening the hive may well chill the brood and kill it. It seems a long list of dislikes, but if it can be remembered that the ideal time for looking at the bees is when the temperature is over 16°C on a mild sunny day, then all will be in the beekeeper's favour.

Before looking into the hive it is as well to check that all the things needed are to hand. After putting on the overall, veil and gloves (if you are going to wear gloves) make sure the smoker is well alight, check matches and extra smoker fuel. This is where pockets on an overall can come in handy. Some beekeepers make themselves a work-box that holds all the things they require. Others find a box just one more thing to fall over! However, make sure that that essential piece of equipment, the hive tool, is with you. Most hive tools are brightly painted, making them easy to spot if dropped in the long grass. Some beekeepers find the ruler pocket on the leg of their boiler suit an ideal place to keep one.

A gentle touch on the roof of the hive and the bees will know you are there. Smoke three or four puffs in at the entrance of the hive. Stand behind the hive and wait a minute or so for the bees to react to the smoke. They do this by filling their honey stomachs from the nearest open cell. This is thought to make them less likely to sting. Much of the bees' reaction to smoke is still a mystery. Probably, in their 'wild' state a forest fire would be a constant threat to their home and in the event of evacuation the bees need to take with them honey, giving them the ability to make comb quickly, this being the only means of colony survival in these circumstances.

Having given the bees time to react to the smoke, take off the roof and place it upside down on the ground next to you behind the hive. This provides a convenient resting place for other parts of the hive. Supers can be stacked here at an angle across the roof with little chance of crushing any bees (see Figure 24). This also applies if the brood chamber is moved off the floor; the upside-down lid would catch the queen in the unlikely event of her falling off the combs. She is so easily lost in the grass. Assuming for the moment there are no supers, the hive tool should be inserted under one corner of the crown board. Then, using the hive tool as a lever, the crown board should be prised off sufficiently to send a puff of smoke from the smoker through the gap across the top of the frames. Gently lift off the crown board. (It is at this stage that one becomes aware that to do this properly you need to grow another pair of hands!) The smoker needs to be put down somewhere to hand where it will not get knocked over as smokers are inclined to go out if laid on their side. Some beekeepers have a hook screwed on to the bellows so that the smoker can be hung on

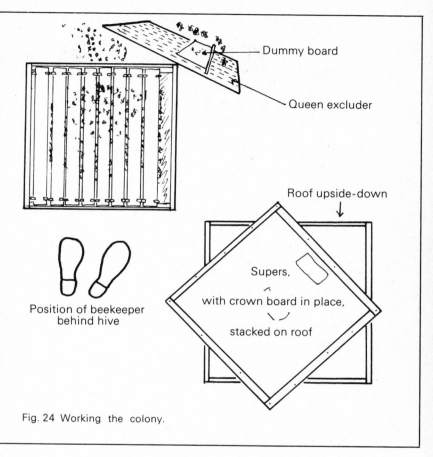

Fig. 24 Working the colony.

Labels in figure: Dummy board; Queen excluder; Roof upside-down; Supers, with crown board in place, stacked on roof; Position of beekeeper behind hive

the side of the hive but this can be inconvenient and many beekeepers keep their smoker gripped by the bellows between their knees where it is always to hand. Having prised off the crown board the underside must be inspected carefully in case the queen is there. If she is, gently pick her off and place her on top of the frames. Place the crown board in front of and leaning up against the front of the hive at an angle so

67

as not to block the entrance. This serves two purposes. Any returning bees that have not been smoked are more inclined to investigate the board and not you and if by any chance the queen was missed and is there on the board she can walk up onto the front of the hive and then onto the top of the frames. These and other precautions regarding the queen after a while become automatic.

Gently smoke across the tops of the frames and using the hive tool prise out the flank comb or dummy board. The dummy board has the advantage that not many bees will be on it and it can be taken from the hive without rolling the bees between the faces of the frames which, not surprisingly, they do not like! Lean the dummy board or flank comb gently against the crown board first making sure the queen is not on it (see Figure 24). There is now plenty of working room in the hive. Little smoke will be required as the bees will only need to be smoked if too many of their numbers 'boil up' over the top of the frames. The frames can now be taken out and looked at. Make sure all your movements are steady and gentle. Try not to pass your hands with quick movements across the tops of the frames. Lift out the frames vertically without rubbing the sides of the frames against the inner wall of the brood chamber and without rubbing the faces of the combs together. A little experience and the frames can be lifted out gently, easily, and steadily. Hold the frames by the lugs at the end of the top bar. Look at both sides of the frame. Place the frame back in the hive in the space that was occupied by the dummy board. Take out the next frame, inspect and replace it up against the frame already inspected making sure not to crush any bees between the self-spacing shoulders. Make sure also that each frame goes back as it came out with the same faces next to one another. When all the frames have been inspected the space will now be at the other side of the hive. All the frames can be shunted back to their original place together rather than one at a time (see Figure 25). This avoids moving each frame individually again and one only has to watch two places—the shoulders of the end frame—where the bees might be crushed.

Any adhering bees can be shaken off the dummy board into the brood chamber and the board replaced. A few gentle puffs of smoke to clear the tops of the frames and these can be scraped clean with the hive tool. Any bees still on the crown board can be knocked off into the brood chamber; it can then be scraped clean. A gentle puff of smoke across the top of the

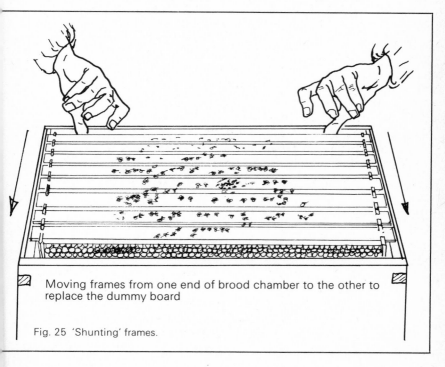

Moving frames from one end of brood chamber to the other to replace the dummy board

Fig. 25 'Shunting' frames.

frames to make the bees duck their heads and the crown board can be replaced, putting one edge down first, avoiding any bees, and gently lowering the crown board onto the brood chamber. When it is almost flush lift it a little and lower it again several times. This will allow any bees that have got in the way time to move and they will not be crushed. This method of putting parts of the hive back together takes less time than it does to write about it and it does avoid crushing bees. Finally the roof can be replaced. Do not despair if you have not the courage on the first inspection to get beyond the first few frames. Gently close down the hive and have another go a week later. Remember it is not essential to look at every frame unless there is a specific reason for doing so.

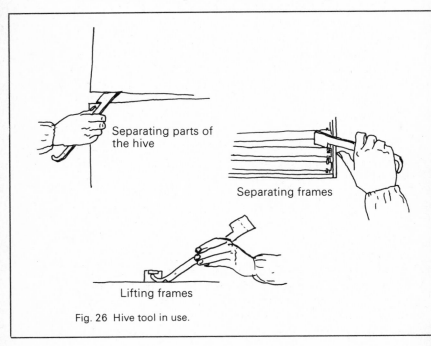

Separating parts of the hive

Separating frames

Lifting frames

Fig. 26 Hive tool in use.

If the hive has supers on, the method of inspection is the same except that the supers intervene between the roof and the brood chamber. After removing the roof and turning it upside down on the ground behind the hive, split the hive between the supers and the brood chamber inserting the hive tool above the queen excluder. Using the hive tool as a lever (see Figure 26) prise up the supers sufficiently to puff smoke in. This drives the bees up into the supers and down into the brood chamber. Put the smoker down and take the weight of the supers with this free hand, remove the hive tool and put it in its place, then there are two hands to lift the supers off and place them on the upturned roof. The crown board on top of the supers need never be removed during this inspection and, of course, keeps the bees in the supers. They will need no attention while the brood chamber is being inspected. The queen excluder can now be treated as was the crown board in the inspection without supers. Smoke can be puffed through the queen excluder to encourage the bees to go down. The queen excluder is removed carefully and inspected on the underside for the queen and then placed in front of the hive as was the crown board. After inspecting the frames in the brood chamber shake the bees off the queen excluder over the brood chamber and scrape off any burr comb or propolis before replacing. The supers can then be replaced using the same method as was described in replacing the crown board, to avoid crushing bees.

Supering

Supering ahead of the bees' requirements and thus giving them plenty of room is one of the practices that help prevent swarming. When the bees are crowding on to the outer comb in the brood chamber they will need a super. Remember you will need a queen excluder as well as a super when putting on the first super of the season. A puff of smoke at the entrance, then remove the roof and crown board in the usual way. Before placing the queen excluder on, it is as well to shake all the bees into the brood chamber from the crown board, even if it is certain the queen is not on there, to make sure the queen does not get isolated from the brood chamber above the queen excluder. The crown board goes on top of the super and the super goes on the queen excluder. The slots in the queen excluder should run at right angles to the frames. The frames in the super should run the same way as the frames in the brood chamber.

The queen excluder acts as a barrier between the brood chamber and the supers so it is as well to try to make the bees' passage through the queen excluder as easy as possible. When the queen excluder is placed with its slots at right angles to the tops of the brood frames it gives a larger area of holes for the bees to go through. Some queen excluders, like the 'Waldron', are made from a wire grid which is framed to give bees space between the excluder and the frames and thus giving the bees access to all the slots. Some bee-keepers frame their zinc or plastic excluders for the same reason. When the zinc, and to a lesser extent the plastic, excluder is made, a press cuts out the slots leaving a rough edge on the underside of the slots. If you run your fingers over the surface of a new excluder this roughness is easily felt. It is thought to be of some help to the bees if this surface is uppermost when it is placed on the hive. The bees going up to the supers will have their honey stomachs full and the rough edges of the slot discourages the bees from going through. When travelling down from the super into the brood chamber the bee is usually 'empty' and so finds the passage through the queen excluder easier and is not put off by the rough edges of the slot. The surface of the queen excluder that you want uppermost can easily be identified by putting a small mark of colourful paint on the border.

When the bees are crowding onto the outer combs of the first super it is time to fit the second one. If the brood chamber is not to be inspected, a puff of smoke at the entrance to warn the bees is all the disturbance the brood chamber requires. Gently prise off the crown board, give a puff of smoke across the top of the frames and the second super can be placed on the first. The crown board is put on top of the second super and the roof replaced. If possible always put supers with undrawn comb (foundation that has not been drawn out) on top of supers with drawn comb. After the bees have worked and drawn out the wax the top super can be exchanged with the bottom super. This puts what was the top super next to the brood chamber above the queen excluder. This may encourage the bees to 'finish off' the wax in the unfinished frames. This method of top supering with undrawn foundation is particularly important when working 'cut comb' as part of the honey production, which is described in detail in the chapter on honey production. Full-size strong colonies at the height of summer may require three or four supers, and in a good season may well fill them with honey!

Stings

Bees sting. All beekeepers get stung. Many bee-keepers do not get stung very often. Even those beekeepers with colonies numbering in the hundreds may receive only six or seven stings after inspecting twenty or thirty colonies, and with about sixty thousand bees in each colony there are an awful lot of potential stings! This is to illustrate how infrequently bees sting. However, if stung on the hand when inspecting a frame it is as well not to drop it. It takes courage and stoicism when first being stung to replace the frame quickly and gently back into the brood chamber and then remove the sting. The sting is best scraped away with the sharp edge of the hive tool. The bee's sting often gets torn away from her body with the poison sac attached. If the sting is scraped off not much poison gets into the skin, but if the sting is pinched between thumb and finger when removing it, most of the bee venom will be injected. Very often there is a swelling but after a little while and a few stings an immunity builds up and the stings have little effect. Relief from the irritation of a sting can be achieved by the application of some anti-histamine cream. 'Anthisan' made by May and Baker is one that is sold by most chemists. If in the unlucky and unlikely event that you are allergic to bee stings you must take very strict precautions against being stung or else give up beekeeping. However, the number of people who are allergic to bee stings is, happily, very few.

Taking a swarm

Despite all precautions, when the inevitable happens and the bees swarm it is to be hoped they find a convenient resting place where they can be taken easily. Perhaps the most convenient is on a low branch of a young tree (see Figure 27(a)). However, what is convenient to the beekeeper is not necessarily most attractive to the bees, and they will swarm onto posts, in thickets and hedges, and even on the ground (see Figures 27(b) and (c)). It would be impossible to list all the places bees can swarm to or how to deal with them. It is at this time that a beekeeper must be most ingenious, as the getting of each swarm poses a different problem.

When taking a swarm from a branch of a tree the best container is probably a skep. This is the ancient form of beehive made of straw. It is light, strong, and

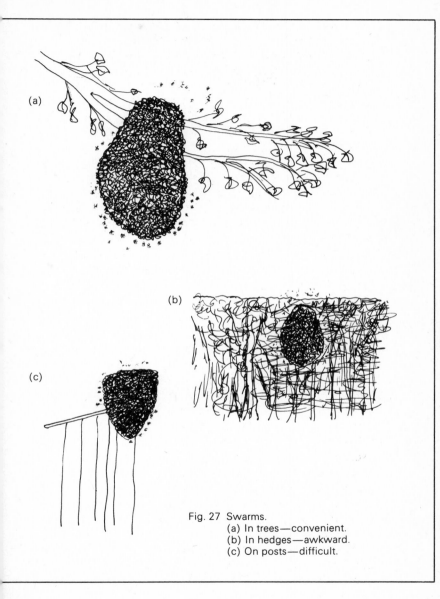

(a)

(b)

(c)

Fig. 27 Swarms.
    (a) In trees—convenient.
    (b) In hedges—awkward.
    (c) On posts—difficult.

75

has a wide 'mouth' like a basket. The roughness of texture gives the bees a good grip when clinging to the interior. A light wooden box or cardboard carton will do the job. Having dressed in beekeeping gear and got the smoker going, the only other things needed are the skep, a piece of wood or a stone to act as a wedge, and a sheet of sacking or cloth big enough to cover the mouth of the skep. The bees having swarmed are usually in a docile, happy mood. The skep can be held upside down under the swarm enveloping most of the cluster of bees. The branch can then be given a sharp shake and the bees will drop into the skep (see Figure 28(a)). Be ready for a sudden increase in weight, particularly if the swarm is high in the tree and is being taken on a ladder! Put the skep on the ground; place the cloth over the mouth of the skep, taut like a jam-pot cover, and turn the skep over. Then prop the mouth of the skep open with the wedge of wood or a stone. The bees will soon be 'fanning' at the entrance to call in the loose bees flying around. The few remaining bees left on the branch can be smoked off. The swarm can now be left until evening when it can be hived. If the queen should be left with a small number of bees clustered on the branch the bees in the skep will leave to rejoin her. Some beekeepers hive the bees as soon as they are sure the queen is in the skep and most of the bees are settled with her.

When the swarm is in the middle of a bush they can sometimes be persuaded into the skep by smoking the cluster from below. This is a slow process since the bees are reluctant to move. Sometimes the bees can be enticed up into a nucleus box or brood chamber by placing a frame of drawn comb or brood in it. There needs to be contact between the swarm and the box and the bees will need a little smoke to get them moving. Once moving they can, quite often, be left to take up residence in the box (see Figure 28(b)).

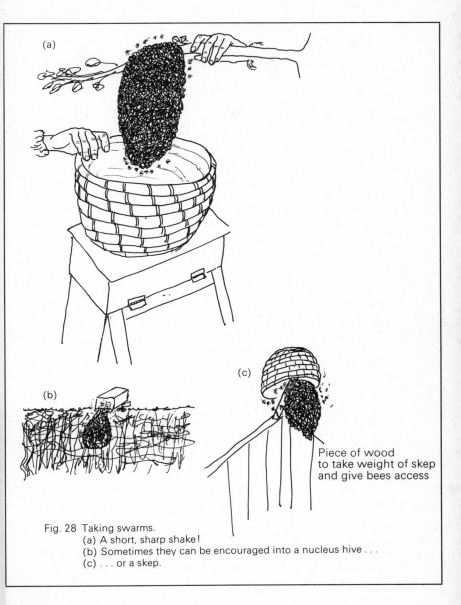

Fig. 28 Taking swarms.
(a) A short, sharp shake!
(b) Sometimes they can be encouraged into a nucleus hive . . .
(c) . . . or a skep.

Piece of wood
to take weight of skep
and give bees access

A swarm on the ground can easily be taken by placing a skep over it. The bees will crawl into the skep and hang there. A swarm on a post may be taken by putting the skep or box underneath the cluster up against the post and sweeping the bees downwards into it. A goose quill, bee brush, or even a tuft of grass will do the job very well. Once most of the bees have been swept into the skep it can be placed on the ground as already described until all the bees have been 'called in'.

The swarm can be put back onto the site it came from in a new brood chamber—the old brood chamber, from which the bees swarmed, being placed on a new site. In this way the swarm and all the flying bees from the removed brood chamber will continue to work in the hive with no loss of nectar gathering. So after smoking the colony in the usual way, remove the roof, supers and queen excluder. Take the brood chamber and put it on a new site with a new floor, crown board and roof. Take out one frame of brood, *but no queen cells*, close up the frames and put in a frame with foundation to fill the space left by the removal of one frame. Put on the crown board and roof and leave. This colony will now produce its own queen. On the original site put the new brood chamber with one frame of brood and the rest of the chamber filled with frames of foundation. Put on the queen excluder, supers and roof. Take out the entrance block. Place a board at the front of the hive sloping up from the ground to the entrance. Uncover the skep, hold it over the board mouth downwards and give it a sharp shake. Most of the bees will drop onto the board and begin to walk up and in at the entrance (see Figure 29). Soon the leading bees will be 'fanning' at the entrance calling in the other bees. Give the skep several sharp taps to dislodge the remaining bees over the board. When the bees are in, the entrance block can be replaced so the size of the entrance is reduced. The bees will now give up swarming since there is plenty of room in the brood chamber. The frame of brood will encourage them to stay. This method of management is very much like the artificial swarming method that is described in detail in the chapter on management.

Fig. 29 Hiving swarms.
    (a) Sometimes branches can be cut off and the bees taken directly to a nearby hive.
    (b) Bees shaken from skep on to a sloping board. Bees run up into hive providing there is no gap between board and entrance.

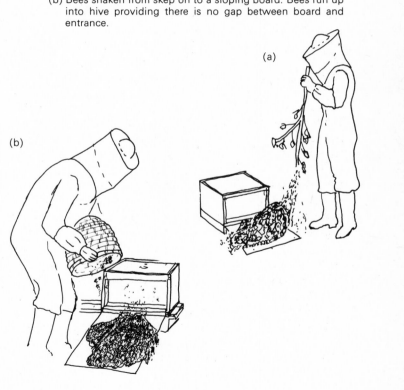

If it is not known from which colony the swarm emerged it would be as well to hive the swarm on the new site. The method is exactly the same except that the bees will be put into a brood chamber containing only frames and foundation. Again, a frame of brood taken from another colony (without queen cells) will encourage them to stay. The swarm in this hive will need feeding with sugar syrup. They will already be 'keen' to build out the foundation and the syrup will be needed to help them to do this work and 'carry them over' until they are settled and able to fend for themselves.

An alternative method is to shake the bees directly into an empty brood chamber or super and then put a brood chamber with frames on top. The bees will soon go up from the empty box below into the one above with the frames. When they are all in, the empty brood chamber or super can be removed.

As has been said, bees are usually docile when they have swarmed, and little smoke is needed when dealing with them. However, always have the smoker going and be ready with a few gentle puffs of smoke to give the bees a little encouragement to go in the direction you want them. Do not be tempted to work without a veil even though the bees are calm. An odd sting near the eye can make you look like a prizefighter for a day or two and one's eyes are too precious to risk.

6 Honey Harvest

The supers of honey are usually taken off the hive at the end of the season: the end of August or beginning of September, depending on the season and the state of the honey.

If three quarters of the honey in the frames has been capped over it can be extracted. Some beekeepers like to leave the frames until all the honey is capped. If the honey cannot be shaken from the uncapped cells it should be right for extraction. If the honey is runny and droplets fall out of the cells when the frame is shaken it still has too high a water content and if extracted in that state will ferment after it has been packed in the jars.

Taking off the honey

To clear the supers of honey a second crown board is required. The crown boards are made to double as clearer boards when Porter bee escapes are placed in the holes (see Figure 30). The bee escape acts as a valve through which the bees can travel down from the supers into the brood chamber, but not back again. To put the clearer board in place, first puff smoke in at the entrance of the hive as usual. Remove the supers in the usual way. Put the clearer board on top of the queen excluder and replace the supers on the clearer board. Make sure that all the parts of the hive are seated properly and there are no gaps or cracks that the bees can enter, since once the supers become clear of bees they become vulnerable to marauding and robbing bees. This is particularly so at the end of the season when there may be no nectar flow and a lot of worker bees hanging around looking for easy pickings. Wasps are also troublesome at this

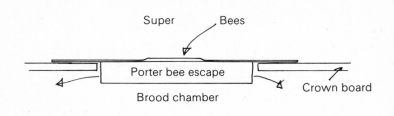

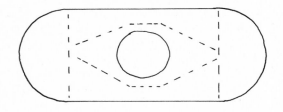

Fig. 30 Porter bee escape.
(a) Side view.
(b) Top view. Springs in bee escape set at about 2 mm. They are flexible and can easily be reset.

time of the year for the same reason. If there is more than one colony on the site it is as well to clear all the hives at the same time. It is best to put the clearer boards on towards dusk when much of the flying has ceased for the day. Twenty-four hours later the bees will have cleared the supers and the supers can be removed. One or two sleepy bees may still be on the combs but these should be no bother as they can be brushed off the combs later.

The supers can be taken away from the apiary and stacked in the room you are going to use for extracting the honey. Make sure the stack of supers is completely 'bee tight' since the smallest gap will be discovered by the bees and they will soon bring all their friends to take the honey back to the hive! Many beekeepers take the cleared supers from the hive in the late evening when most of the flying bees are home for the night. Extracting can then start and, hopefully, be completed well before the bees are out and about again in the morning.

The usual way of dealing with the supers after the honey has been extracted is to place them back on the hive for the bees to clean up. This can be done with little disturbance to the bees if they are placed back on the hive immediately after extracting and before the bees are out. Since the bees will be excited by the sudden appearance of the extracted combs they are more likely to start robbing. If the extracted supers are all placed on one hive this can aggravate the situation. If the extracted supers are distributed round all the hives, all the colonies will be excited and 'on their guard' with less likelihood of being robbed. When placing the supers back on the hive one or both of the bee escapes must be removed from the clearer board to give the bees access to the supers. After twenty-four hours the bee escapes can be put back in the clearer board as the bees will have cleaned up the frames by this time. Again, twenty-four hours later the supers, now cleared of bees, can be removed and they can be stored away until needed the following year.

The supers should be stored in a cool, dry place, one on top of another with a crown board on top and at the bottom of the pile. Make sure there are no small gaps that mice can enter. Sprinkle para-dichlor-benzine (P.D.B.) crystals through the supers to deter wax moth which can eat their way through the wax comb when it is stored over winter.

After the bees have cleaned up the supers and they

have been removed, the queen excluder can be taken off the hive and also the bee escapes in the crown board. These can be cleaned up and stored away ready for next season. The bees are now ready for their winter feeding.

Extracting

For extracting the honey you will need an uncapping knife, an uncapping tray, a honey extractor and a settling tank (see Figures 31 and 33). For packaging the honey for sale, you will need honey jars or similar containers, and labels (see Figure 32).

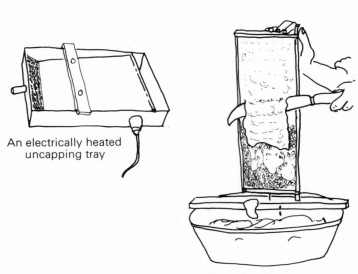

An electrically heated uncapping tray

For small quantities a bowl will be sufficient for the cappings

Fig. 31 Uncapping.

The wax cappings on the honeycomb need to be removed before the honey can be extracted. If the uncapping knife is kept warm it will slice through the wax more easily. If there are only one or two supers to extract an old bread knife kept in a jug of hot water will do the job. Two knives make things easier since one can be heating in the water while the other is being used. The heated uncapping trays sold by the manufacturers have a convenient gap at one end where the knives can be kept in hot water. Wipe the knife dry on a cloth before using.

After removing the spacers on the lugs of the frames, hold the frame over the uncapping tray (a bowl or meat tin will do as an uncapping tray), cut upwards underneath the cappings so they fall into the tray. Do both sides of the frame (see Figure 31). When the frame is uncapped it can be put into the honey extractor. When the extractor is full the handle can be turned and the honey will be flung out into the drum.

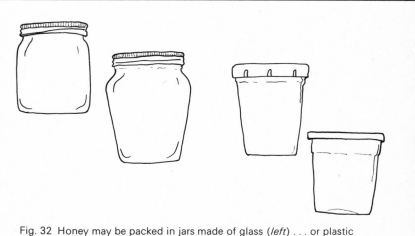

Fig. 32 Honey may be packed in jars made of glass (*left*) . . . or plastic (*right*).

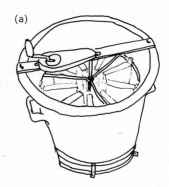

(a)

Honey is strained through cloth

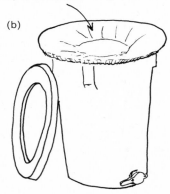

(b)

(c)

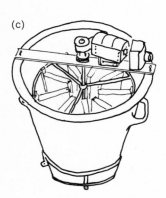

Fig. 33 Extracting equipment.
    (a) A modern hand extractor with a heavy duty polythene barrel.
    (b) Settling tank.
    (c) Some extractors are powered by small electric motors.

Extractors

There are several different types of extractor on the market. Some are made of tin, some of stainless steel and, more recently, some made of heavy duty polythene. Most models are turned by hand but some have a small electric motor to power them (see Figure 33(c)). Two main systems of extraction are used in these extractors—the tangential and the radial systems.

In the tangential system the face of the comb is parallel with the side of the drum (see Figure 34(a)). The frames should be loaded so the bottom of the frame leads in the direction of travel when the cage spins. When half the honey has been extracted from one side of the frame, the frame must be turned over and all the honey spun from the other side. The frame then needs turning over again so that the remainder of the honey can be extracted. If all the honey were extracted from one side first there would be great pressure on the honey on the other side of the frame which could break the comb.

In the radial system the frames are placed in the extractor cage like the spokes of a wheel with the top bar of the frame nearest the side of the drum. Both sides of the frame are extracted at the same time (see Figure 34(b)) and there is, of course, no need to turn the frames over.

During extracting, the honey leaves the comb quite rapidly at first but the cage needs to be kept turning for some time to ensure that all the honey is extracted. It is important to ensure the cage speed does not exceed 400 r.p.m. as speeds much faster than this can shatter the combs. When the honey has been extracted or when the reservoir at the bottom of the extractor is getting full the honey needs to be drained off through the tap into the settling tank (see Figure 33(b)). The honey is strained through the straining

87

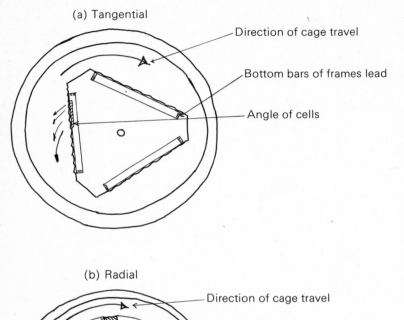

(a) Tangential

Direction of cage travel

Bottom bars of frames lead

Angle of cells

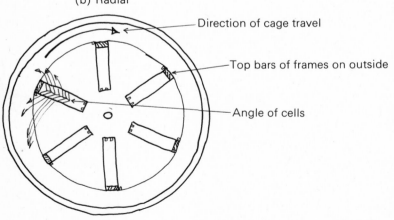

(b) Radial

Direction of cage travel

Top bars of frames on outside

Angle of cells

Fig. 34 Radial and tangential methods of extracting.

cloth and then is allowed to stand for about twenty-four hours to allow the air bubbles to settle out and rise to the surface before bottling.

When the extracting and settling equipment is finished with, it needs to be rinsed out with cold water before washing with warm detergent water. Using cold water first prevents the particles of wax from being melted and spread over the equipment or clogging the straining cloths. The modern polythene barrels used in extractors and settling tanks are very easy to clean and sterilise. All particles made from tin should be thoroughly dried and wiped with a cloth soaked in liquid paraffin in an attempt to prevent the tinware going rusty.

The wax cappings that go through a heated uncapping tray are melted as the frames are uncapped. If the cappings have been collected in a bowl or meat tin they can be rendered into a block by putting them into a mixing bowl and placing the bowl in a warm oven (70°C). When the wax has melted turn off the oven and allow to cool overnight. The wax will form a solid layer on top of a quantity of honey. The honey can be used for the household and the wax saved and exchanged at the suppliers for foundation at a later date.

Honey can be bottled straight from the settling tank. The valve at the bottom of the tank is designed to give control over the speed at which the honey flows. Allowing honey to travel down the side of the jar rather than dropping straight to the bottom prevents air being trapped in the honey (see Figure 35). Some time after it has been bottled the honey will granulate or go solid. All honey (except some heather honey) granulates but some honeys granulate more quickly than others depending on the source of the nectar. Granulation is a natural process in which the sugars in the honey solidify.

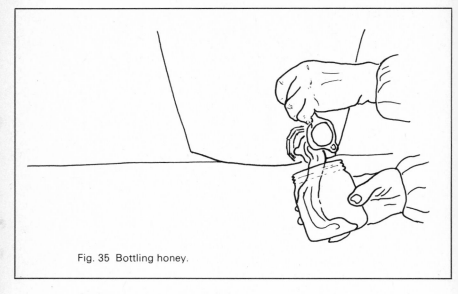

Fig. 35 Bottling honey.

Bottling and labelling

When the honey jars are labelled, the honey is ready
for sale. If the honey is sold through a shop it must
have the name and address of the producer or supplier
printed or written on the label. The label must also
state the net weight of the honey and, of course, the jar
must contain the weight it says it does. The description of the honey on the jar must be an accurate
description of the contents. If it says 'Shropshire
Honey' on the jar, the jar must contain Shropshire
honey. If it says English Honey it must be English and
not Welsh or Scottish honey, and so on. At the
moment honey must be packed in lbs, $\frac{1}{2}$ lbs, or equal
divisions of a lb or whole numbers of lbs. These are
the regulations under the various Acts relating to the
description of goods, pure food and drugs, and
weights and measures. These regulations may well
change now we are in the Common Market.

Heather honey

Heather honey is different from other honeys. It is thixotropic in behaviour and is therefore difficult to extract in the normal way. It can be scraped off the frames, honey and wax together, and then heated to separate the wax and the honey. Alternatively the whole of the honeycomb can be removed from the frame and the honey extracted in a honey press. In a third method the honey can be broken down from its jelly-like characteristic to a liquid form by agitation. This can be done in the comb by a tool called a perforextractor. The combs can then be extracted in an ordinary honey extractor.

Cut comb honey

This sort of honey production has become very popular during the past few years. There is a ready market for whole honeycomb. The only disadvantage is that the wax foundation needs replacing every year.

Cut comb honey production starts in the spring when extra thin unwired wax foundation is fitted into the super frames. When putting the supers on the hive the undrawn foundation should always go on top. Never put a super of undrawn foundation between the brood chamber and the super the bees are already working in. When the foundation has been well started by the bees and they are beginning to fill it, then it can be placed just above the brood chamber. This will encourage the bees to fill the frames completely.

When the supers are filled they can be taken from the hive in the usual way. It is sometimes advisable to remove the frames being used for cut comb production fairly early in the season as soon as most of the frames have been capped over. Those frames not capped can be returned in the centre of the super flanked by more foundation ready for the bees to do

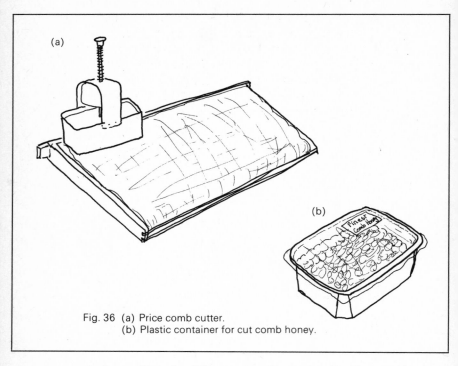

Fig. 36 (a) Price comb cutter.
(b) Plastic container for cut comb honey.

their work again. The reason for removing the combs early is to preserve the attractive appearance of the comb. The passage of many little feet over the face of the comb tends to darken it. To do all the wax working needed for this sort of honey production the colony must be very strong in numbers and there must be plenty of nectar coming in.

Processing cut comb honey is very simple with the aid of a Price comb cutter (see Figure 36(a)). The frame of honeycomb is laid down on an even, clean surface such as a chopping board and with the cutter the comb can be cut from the frame and ejected into a plastic container (see Figure 36(b)), without the comb being fingered or handled. This method is very quick and six blocks of cut comb honey can be cut from a well-capped standard shallow frame. The cutter is the only tool needed for this sort of honey production. It is, of course, possible, though messier, to cut out the comb with a sharp, long-bladed knife. The container must state what it holds and the name and address of the producer/supplier needs to be shown but it is not necessary to state the weight of the contents.

7 Bee Diseases and Enemies

More colonies of bees die through starvation than from all the diseases they are prone to put together. This is due mainly to neglect on behalf of the beekeeper who should be the bees' best friend not their worst enemy. But it is a sad fact that many beekeepers, having taken off the honey, do nothing to repay the bees who are left to fend for themselves at a time of the year when there is very little for them to gather and to make a sensible surplus to last the winter.

Apart from man the bees in this country have very few real enemies. Blue Tits have been known to tap at the entrance of the hive in cold weather and when a sleepy guard bee comes out to see what is going on the Blue Tit pecks up a tasty meal. Others in the Tit family are also known to do this but they can all be distracted by easier pickings on the bird table. Toads have also been known to sit outside a hive and take workers as they fly home but both of the above do little to reduce the numbers of the colony.

Colonies situated near woods have been known to suffer severely from the attention of woodpeckers who very quickly drill through the hive to get to the bees inside. Once inside they seem to acquire a taste for the honey and will attack hive after hive to get at it. Beekeepers take steps to prevent the damage these birds do by spreading a net over their hives.

Wasps are a menace to small colonies, particularly when these are being fed. The wasps are very persistent and if they arrive in great numbers can soon overpower and rob out a weak or small colony.

There is a small parasite called a bee louse, which is a tiny wingless fly that clings to the back of the thorax of the bee. These lice are not present in all colonies and do not seem to have any detrimental effect on the bees. They move down to the mouth parts of the bee when she is exchanging food to steal a meal from her tongue. Since the queen is being fed most of the time she is likely to be more afflicted with these parasites than the workers. Even she can tolerate a fair number of them before her efficiency is impaired. The eggs of this little parasite are laid on the cappings of the cells and the larvae burrow along the cappings leaving little white trails which look unsightly on a comb of honey. They can be removed by puffing tobacco smoke over the bees. The parasite falls off. If a sheet of newspaper is placed on the floor under the brood chamber during this operation the paper together with the bee lice can be removed and burned. The treatment would need to be carried out several times to get rid of successive generations as they hatch out. It must be emphasised, however, that the bee louse is not a problem in beekeeping as can be some other complaints and diseases.

Diseases of adult bees

Nosema. This also should not be a problem for beekeepers on a small scale who do not have to move their hives. Commercial and semi-commercial bee-keepers who have to move their hives as part of their business are sometimes plagued with this disease which, at times, can cause serious losses among their bees. Moving the hive aggravates the situation. Nosema affects adult bees of all ages and is mostly prevalent during spring—April to June, although it may occur later. It is a condition caused by a microscopic parasite that is active in the mid-gut of the bee. This gives the bee an upset tummy and it is unable to control its bodily functions and voids excreta on the comb. Bees, being clean creatures in the hive, clean up the mess and so the parasite is passed from bee to bee very rapidly. This condition is particularly aggravated if the bees are confined to the hive for any length of time. If the bees are upset or excited this also causes them to void on the comb with the consequent spread of infection. Probably the first sign that there is anything wrong is the dwindling number of bees. Spots of excreta on the combs, watery and pale grey in colour, are a surer sign. The bees themselves, when they are badly affected, crawl about outside the hive, trembling, and eventually die on their backs with their legs in the air. Nosema can be treated by a drug called Fumagillin which is marketed as 'Fumidil B' obtainable from E. H. Thorpe, Wragby, Lincoln. The drug is administered by being mixed with sugar syrup and fed to the bees in the normal way. This cures the Nosema in the bees but the badly fouled combs need to be replaced.

To do this put the queen on her comb, flanked by frames of foundation, in a clean brood chamber on top of the contaminated brood chamber with a queen excluder between. When the queen has moved off her frame and is laying in the new comb, the frame she was moved on can be replaced in the lower chamber. All the brood in the lower chamber will emerge and the young bees will go up with the queen. When all the brood cells are empty in the bottom chamber it can be removed and sterilised.

The contaminated frames and brood chamber can be sterilised by placing them away from the bees on a floor with the entrance closed and a well-fitting crown board and roof to make the whole completely bee-proof. Before closing down, a large pad of cotton wool is placed on top of the frames under the crown board and the pad is soaked with $\frac{1}{4}$ litre of 80 per cent acetic acid. Make sure the hive is closed down properly; leave alone for a fortnight. The fumes from the acetic acid will fumigate the frames and the brood chamber. The frames can now be used again after they have been aired for twenty-four hours. Although bee-keepers with two or three colonies who do not move their hives may never come across Nosema, the disease is on the increase and can become a menace.

Acarine. Acarine, on the other hand, seems to be on the decline. Treating colonies was once a regular feature of the beekeeper's calendar. It says much for those who have tried to rear Acarine-resistant strains of bee, and beekeepers' diligence in treating the complaint, that it is on the decline. These two factors have probably done much to control a condition that practically wiped out the whole of the honeybee population in the British Isles at about the time of the First World War. It started in the Isle of Wight and for many years was called Isle of Wight disease.

Acarine is caused by a parasitic mite entering the breathing tubes in the thorax of the adult bee, taking up residence there, feeding on the tissue, and multiplying at a rapid rate to the detriment of the bee. The mite can only get into the breathing tube of the bee during the first five days of the bee's life when the small hairs that protect the opening are still soft. The bees show signs of being infected when they crawl about in numbers in front of the hive with dislocated wings, a conditions known as 'K wing'—which describes it exactly.

Treatment of the condition is usually done with Frow mixture. This can be bought from appliance manufacturers or the local beekeepers' association. The treatment is carried out in either November or February during a long cold spell when the bees are not flying. The Frow mixture, which is a liquid, can be soaked into a pad which is placed in the feed hole of the crown board. The pad is left in place for about a fortnight. The fumes from the Frow mixture are thought to kill the mite.

If there is any doubt about why bees have died, a sample of bees can be sent to the local County Beekeeping Instructor/Advisor who will diagnose any disease and give advice. This service is free of charge and the C.B.I.'s address can be obtained from the local beekeepers' association or the Beekeeping Advisor of the Agricultural Department Advisory Service whose address is at the back of this book. When sending bees for analysis try to select those that have recently died. Put about twenty-five bees in a matchbox and send two or three matchboxes if possible. Never pack dead bees in a polythene bag. The bees deteriorate very quickly once air is excluded and it presents the examiner with a very smelly, messy package to sort out. Put the matchboxes in an envelope with BEES in capital letters in the top left-hand corner and it is surprising how gently the package is handled by the Post Office!

Diseases of the brood

American Foul Brood (A.F.B.) and European Foul Brood (E.F.B.) are the two most prevalent diseases of brood and they are the most serious. A.F.B. is widespread throughout the British Isles. E.F.B. is less widespread but is highly infectious where it does occur, spreading to other nearby colonies where it may remain undetected for a season or more.

American Foul Brood. A.F.B. is caused by a micro-scopic spore-forming organism. It affects the sealed brood and is spread throughout the colony by bees cleaning up cells containing an infected larva and then going on to feed young larvae in other cells. The larva collapses and dies within the capped cell. The cell cappings become sunken and have holes in them where the bees try to break down the diseased larva and remove it (see Figure 37(a)). The larva collapses, turns dark brown then black and lies along the base of the cell. It smells of bad glue but the smell is not always strong. The remains of the larva stick tightly to the cell and when tested, by poking the cell with a matchstick, will form a 'rope' (see Figure.37(b)).

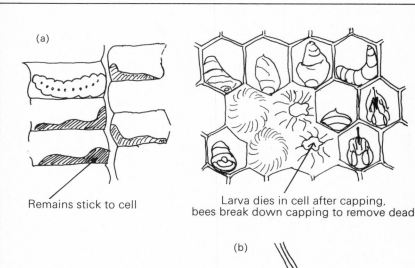

(a)

Remains stick to cell

Larva dies in cell after capping, bees break down capping to remove dead

(b)

Fig. 37 American foul brood.
(a) Appearance of cells.
(b) 'Rope' test.

European Foul Brood. E.F.B. is caused by a bacterial infection of the young larva in the early stage of larval development, so the larva dies before it is capped over. The larva, instead of resting in the normal position, seem to move about in a restless way and form unusual positions in the cells. The larva goes yellow in colour, then brown. There may be a slight 'sour' odour about the frames. The diseased larvae are easily removed from the cells, which the bees do readily, giving the frame a 'pepper pot' appearance with the empty cells scattered amongst large patches of sealed brood.

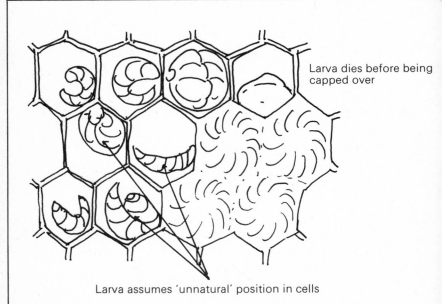

Larva dies before being capped over

Larva assumes 'unnatural' position in cells

Fig. 38 European foul brood.

The Foul Brood Disease Order 1967. When Foul Brood is discovered it is best to report it rather as pigkeepers must report swine fever, chicken farmers must report fowl pest, and cattle farmers must report foot and mouth disease.

Under the Foul Brood Diseases Order the Ministry of Agriculture has the power to inspect colonies of bees and take samples for analysis. The Ministry has appointed Bees Officers to do the work. When Foul Brood is discovered the colonies infected must be destroyed (in the case of A.F.B.) or treated (in the case of E.F.B.) under the supervision of the Bees Officer. There is no compulsory registration of beekeepers so the Ministry relies on the co-operation of beekeepers so that regular inspections of apiaries can take place—to the obvious advantage of the beekeepers. Membership of the local Beekeepers' Association in most cases gives automatic insurance cover against Foul Brood through Bee Diseases Insurance Ltd. from whom extra insurance can be obtained for a larger number of colonies.

Other Brood Diseases

Chalk Brood. This is caused by a fungus and affects the sealed larva which turns yellow then white and fluffy and finally white or grey. There is no odour and when the bees uncap the cells to remove the remains they are seen to be hard, smooth and white with the consistency of broken biscuit or chalk. As with many of these minor disorders the remedy is to re-queen the colony, and this will be so until research in this field comes up with an effective remedy.

Sac Brood. Sac Brood is caused by a virus infection which affects the sealed brood before it pupates. The brood goes a dark yellow colour. There is no smell.

The larval skin forms a sac which is filled with a watery fluid which is easily removed from the cell. The remedy is to re-queen.

Addled Brood. Addled Brood affects the sealed pupa when it is almost fully developed as a bee. Small, shrunken, fully developed bees are found dead in their cells. This is caused by a genetic fault in the queen and she should be replaced. There is no smell.

These last three brood disorders, in the main, affect only isolated cells scattered throughout the frames.

Chilled Brood. This is a condition and not a disease. It affects brood in all stages of development, including eggs. All the brood over a large area of the comb is usually dead. Its colour is white, grey or black and there is no smell. Chilled brood can be caused by the beekeeper opening the hive and inspecting the brood when the temperature is low. It can also occur when the brood nest has expanded during a mild spell in early spring and this is followed by a cold period. The bees contract their cluster to preserve warmth and areas of brood may be left outside this cluster and become chilled.

Many beekeepers have for many years kept bees and never seen the diseases and disorders mentioned here. Remember that man probably causes more deaths to bees and colonies through mishandling and mismanagement than all the diseases put together.

8 Apiary and Hive Hygiene

Most diseases and detrimental conditions can be prevented by attention to cleanliness and order within the hive and apiary.

Always keep the apiary tidy. Never throw down propolis and brace comb that has been scraped from the frames and other parts of the hive. Always be careful when feeding the bees that no sugar syrup is slopped about as all these things tend to attract inquisitive bees who may be looking nearby for easy pickings and robbing will soon start in the apiary. Apart from the detrimental effect on the bees being robbed, the robbers could easily pick up any disease or complaint and spread it to their own hives.

Never buy old combs or colonies of bees unless it is known that they come from disease-free apiaries. This also applies to swarms. Whether to accept a swarm or not is a very difficult decision to make when one is starting beekeeping. The swarm offered can be such a good way of starting beekeeping but it must be said that many potential beekeepers have been discouraged when the swarm that seemed such a good thing in May becomes a disease-ridden, unproductive problem by the end of July with the consequent loss of frames that have to be burned because the swarm brought Foul Brood with it. The only 'safe' swarm is the one you know came from your own disease-free hive!

Second-hand hives and equipment must always be sterilised before use even if they were given to you by your best friend. All wooden hive parts can be scorched with a blow lamp, particular attention being paid to joints, cracks and crevices. Hive tools and smokers can be scrubbed with a diluted solution of Jeyes' fluid. Honey-extracting and -settling equipment should be washed thoroughly. Washing soda in the water helps to clean out the joints and folds in the tinware. Make sure the equipment is thoroughly dry before storing away, as explained in the chapter on honey production. Plastic equipment is very easy to sterilise. Once it has been washed out it can be rinsed with a solution of hyperchlorite as is used on dairy farms for sterilising milking equipment. A more easily available form of hyperchlorite is Milton which is used for sterilising babies' bottles.

Never feed bees on honey from an unknown source since Foul Brood spores can be carried in this way.

If a colony dies out during the winter through starvation, take no chances and treat the frames and hive as if it had Nosema. The treatment is described in full in the chapter on diseases.

When visiting other apiaries to help other bee-keepers, never use your own equipment on their bees. Likewise, if someone visits your apiary to help, use your own equipment on your own bees.

Frames within the brood chamber should be replaced when they become mis-shapen or contain too many drone cells. This also applies when they have been in the brood chamber for many years and are dark, tough and now have holes in them where successive generations of queen cells have been removed. Move these combs to the flank of the other frames during the year so they can be replaced in the following spring. In this way the frames in the brood chamber do get renewed and this can safeguard against old combs (which after many years may become infected) being left in the hive.

After a time it is a good thing to acquire spare floors

and crown boards. After a season in use these can be cleaned, sterilised by scorching, and given a coat of creosote. The creosote is not needed to preserve the wood if it is western red cedar, but to complete the sterilising. Creosote is very good at killing off many germs. It is also thought the fumes from the creosoted wood, when placed under the brood chamber in the spring, help to control Acarine. The bees spend much of their time cleaning the floor and sticking down the crown board and if the beekeeper gives these parts of the hive close attention when cleaning this will help to prevent the spread of disease. The cleaned floor boards can be placed on the hive during the first inspection of the year, the old floors being taken away for cleaning and treating.

The feeding buckets made of plastic are easy to clean and sterilise in the same way as described for other plastic equipment. Dirty feeders can be a source of infection for the bees.

In general, any good housekeeping technique that is used in the home if applied to the bees and equipment should become a habit that will help prevent the spread of infection through the apiary.

9 The Beekeeper's Year

It is hoped the sequence of events in a beekeeper's year, which is set out here in a simplified form, will give some indication of the continuity of events in the apiary.

March

In the southern part of the country, towards the end of the month colonies may be examined. This is always providing the day is warm and sunny, that there are no cold winds, that the bees are flying well and there is pollen being brought in. This is an indication that the winter cluster has broken up and the bees can be examined without any detrimental effects. But colonies should not be examined unnecessarily. Ascertain there is a queen present and that there is an adequate amount of stores. The presence of drones may indicate queenlessness or the presence of a drone-laying queen. Queenless colonies should be united with queen-right stocks. In the northern parts of the country the first examination should be put off for a month.

April

In areas of much fruit blossom, when the weather is right and the colonies strong, supers may be required. Thorough examinations of the colony can begin this month and detailed records started.

May

Be on the look-out for signs of swarming which may start early in the month. Make a decision now about any increase in the number of colonies you may want and make preparations by having enough extra equipment. Practise swarm control. Super well ahead of bees' requirements.

June
A 'lull' in the bees' activity associated with a fall in the amount of nectar available may be experienced in this month. In bad years the bees will need keeping a close eye on to make sure the demand for food for brood rearing does not exceed the supply of food coming into the hive. Keep practising swarm control. Super ahead of requirements.

July to August
Work through July as you did in June. July may see an increase again in nectar flow. Remove supers at the end of August or beginning of September. Extracting time.

September to October
Feed the bees. Final inspection of colonies. Ensure they are queen-right and have plenty of stores for the winter. Finish feeding by the end of September if possible. Feeding can continue into the middle of October.

November to February
Do not disturb the bees. Occasionally examine the roofs to make sure they are watertight. If snow should drift against the front of the hive, remove it from the entrance to allow ventilation. Winter is a time for reading and study. Go over the year's records and plan next year's campaign. An ideal time to order equipment—or make your own.

Appendix A

The National Hive

This section together with Figure 39 will, I hope, be of value to those who might want to make their own hive.

Floor. The floor boards are made of 20 mm timber with tongued and grooved or lap joints if possible. These are set into the side rails 6 mm. The side rails are 51 mm by 20 mm. The groove for the floor boards is set at 22 mm down from the surface that will make contact with the brood chamber.

Brood Chamber. The timber used for the side walls and the end walls is 19 mm thick.

Supers. These have exactly the same measurements as the brood chamber apart from the side walls which are 150 mm deep and the end walls that are 128 mm deep.

Roof. The side walls should be 13 mm thick. The roof should be covered with a non-rusting metal cover or other waterproof material. The ventilation holes are 20 mm diameter and are backed by perforated zinc or wire mesh.

Making Up. Use a good-quality waterproof glue. Use rust-proof nails.

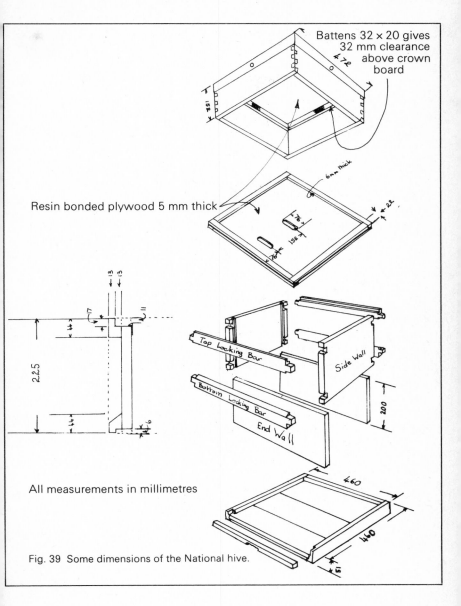

Battens 32 × 20 gives
32 mm clearance
above crown
board

472

152

Resin bonded plywood 5 mm thick

6mm thick

22

76

152

76

13

13

17

11

44

225

44

6

Top Locking Bar

Side Wall

Bottom Locking Bar

End Wall

200

All measurements in millimetres

460

460

15

Fig. 39 Some dimensions of the National hive.

Appendix B

Glossary of Beekeeping Terms and Useful Information

As with other specialised crafts and trades, beekeeping has its own terminology. It is hoped the following glossary, which is not in strict alphabetical order or exhaustive, will be of help to those beginning beekeeping in understanding the conversation and instruction of other beekeepers!

Apiary. A place where bees are kept.

Out apiary. An apiary site some miles away from home.

Artificial swarm. Usually bees plus the queen separated from the combs and brood by the beekeeper. Now also used to denote a method of increasing the number of colonies by removing the queen, some bees and some brood in frames.

Bee space. The general clearance between parts which the bees will respect and in which they will not usually build much wax. This is taken to be between 6 mm and 9 mm. Hive manufacturers use 8 mm as bee space.

Bee way. Space or hole used by the bees for communication and left by them when building comb.

Brace comb. Sometimes called Burr comb and built in odd spaces in the hive particularly where the frames are ill-fitting and leave more than a bee space. This comb is not used for brood rearing but sometimes contains honey.

Wild comb or *Natural comb*. Full-sized sheets of comb built by the bees in their natural state or in a space in the hive where a frame has been left out. It is complete and contains brood in all stages and stores of honey and pollen.

Brood nest. It is usually the area of combs used by the queen and bees to rear brood. The brood nest is therefore of different sizes depending on the season of the year.

Brood frame. A deep frame used for brood rearing, the depth of which is usually about 60 per cent of the length. A shallow frame with a depth of about 50 per cent of the length is used for storing surplus honey. These can also be used as part of the brood area.

Building up. A term used to describe the increase in size of the colony.

Comb. The wax structure of cells built by the bees to contain the brood and hold stores. Sometimes taken to mean a frame of comb.

Drawn comb. Wax foundation in a frame that has been built out from the foundation base is said to be 'Drawn comb' or 'Drawn out'.

Dummy board. A board the same size as the frames used for blanking off a part of the hive when it contains a small colony. Sometimes left in the brood chamber to give working space when inspecting the colony.

Division board. A board the exact dimensions of the interior of the hive used to isolate one part of the brood chamber. Not in wide use these days and then used for special purposes as in queen breeding.

Foundation. A sheet of beeswax with the pattern of cells impressed upon it. Placed in a frame to assist the bees in building comb. It forms the *Septum* or mid-rib of the comb on which the cell walls are built up.

Hive. A box or container in which bees are kept. Sometimes, erroneously, used to describe a stock of bees.

Stock of bees. The hive and its contents including a queen, bees, and brood.

Colony of bees. The queen, bees, and brood on frames or comb. A colony of bees can as well be in a hollow tree as in a hive.

Honey flow. A misnomer. The proper term should probably be 'Nectar flow' as it describes the copious secretion of nectar by plants and the subsequent frantic activity of the bees in collecting it.

Honey Dew. A sweet substance produced from the extra floral nectaries in plants and from aphids feeding on plants. The bees collect this substance and treat it as they do nectar.

Handling. The act of moving the bees and frames when inspecting the colony.

Increase. The production of more colonies.

Migration or *Migratory beekeeping*. A term used when stocks are moved to crops at another location.

Nucleus. A small colony of bees. The British Standard Specification/B.S.S. 1372: 1947 is briefly as follows: There should be a mated laying queen, worker brood in all stages in at least half the comb area, an average of 0.56 kg of honey and pollen per comb and enough bees to cover all the combs. There should be no visible signs of disease. The above refers to nuclei offered for sale. Nuclei are also used in the apiary for rearing queens and will therefore be different from the B.S.S. standard.

Prime swarm. The first swarm to leave the hive with the old queen. If a colony swarms again the second swarm is called a *Cast*. Subsequent swarms from the same colony are sometimes called *Colts*. These tend to be very small indeed.

Queen-right. A term used to denote that the colony has a mated, laying queen.

Skep. An old type of beehive made usually of straw, roughly conical in shape. Useful for catching swarms.

Uniting. Putting two lots of bees together with one queen. A queenless colony can be united with a queen-right colony.

Virgin. Properly—virgin queen. Used to describe an unmated queen.

Information that may be of interest

Comb spacing. This varies slightly with the types of frames used. B.S. frames with spacers are 38 mm from the centre line of one top bar to the centre line of the next (from septum to septum). This spacing will be a little narrower on self-spacing frames.

Weight of a swarm. Bees weigh roughly 10,000 to the kilogramme, so a 2½ kg swarm will have about 25,000 bees.

Nectar-carrying capacity of bees. About 40 milligrams as a usual full load but the bees hold much more after being smoked when they gorge themselves and can take up to 100 milligrams.

Capacity of frames. A B.S. deep frame has about 4,500 cells and will hold in the region of 2.25 kg of honey when full. The B.S. shallow frame will hold about 1.33 kg of honey when full.

Melting temperature of wax. About 63°C. It is moulded by the bees at around 35°C. To produce a kilogramme of wax it is thought the bees consume between $4\frac{1}{2}$ kg and 18 kg of honey. The lower figure probably refers to a very strong colony producing wax under normal circumstances.

Odds and ends

For the weight of a hive to increase during a nectar flow at the rate of 2 kg a day, bees need to be leaving and returning to the hive at a rate of 3 per second during a 10-hour day.

Bees can travel economically up to 2 miles from the hive on foraging flights.

For every kg of ripened honey, between 99,000 and 154,000 bee journeys are made. If the average journey is one mile, that is in the region of 126,500 bee-miles per kg of honey!

It is possible that a colony of bees uses in the region of 1 litre of water per day at the height of summer.

The amount of pollen used by the bees in a year may be in the region of 45 kg.

Appendix C

Flowers, Shrubs and Trees Useful to Bees

Bees, other pollinating insects, and flowers have evolved together—each requiring the services of the other. Flowers provide food for the bees in the form of nectar and pollen and the bees provide a pollinating service to the plant.

Some of the flowers listed below are grown as an agricultural crop and are unlikely to be found in a suburban area. But there are many flowers like crocus, shrubs like buddleia, and trees like sumach which, when repeated in garden after garden, provide a very useful source of forage for the bees. Many of the trees mentioned can be found in abundance in a suburban as well as a rural environment. The list is obviously by no means exhaustive but gives an indication of the variety of flowers visited by bees.

Flowers

Aconite and Crocus. These are a good source of early pollen.

Poppy. An example of a plant providing exclusively pollen as a food source for bees.

Michaelmas Daisy. An example of a late-flowering plant that is very useful to bees for both pollen and nectar.

Dandelion. A very good flower for the honey bee since it produces nectar and pollen in abundance.

Lucerne. This is a field crop that is grown for animal fodder. When it is allowed to flower it produces nectar copiously.

Field Bean. This is also a field crop and provides much of the protein in animal foodstuffs. This crop often yields a lot of nectar and the bees provide a valuable pollinating service to the farmer.

Mustard. Rich in pollen and nectar, the produce of this plant is grown for human consumption along with roast beef!

Charlock. A weed that once provided many bee-keepers with a good supply of honey. Now rarely seen due to good husbandry on the part of the farmer. Where it does occur it is a very reliable source of nectar and pollen.

Oilseed Rape. Rapidly becoming a very popular field crop with many farmers. It is very attractive to bees for both nectar and pollen. The honey made from the nectar of this plant must be removed by the beekeeper soon after it is capped over as the honey granulates very quickly.

Clover. This plant, along with others in the family, like Sainfoin and Sweet Clover (Melilot), provide the main nectar source for many beekeeping enterprises not only in this country but throughout the world.

Rosebay Willowherb. Taking over disaster areas such as stretches of woodland and heath after fires and many other neglected areas, this plant is a valuable source of nectar and pollen. The plant conveniently flowers over a long period with new flowers appearing as others die off.

Seed Crops. Cabbage, and other crops like turnip, carrot, radish are sometimes grown for seed. The extra acreage of flowers can be a bonus for any beekeeper in the area!

Shrubs and other plants

Blackberry. This plant, that seems to grow everywhere and anywhere and flowers over a long period, is a valuable source of nectar and pollen.

Soft Fruits. Blackcurrants, redcurrants, gooseberries, raspberries, strawberries and so on are all very attractive to honeybees. They all provide nectar and pollen and any gardener who has noticed the increase in his crops of soft fruit knows how valuable the honeybees are.

Hawthorn. This hedge plant tends to be fickle. Some years it produces nectar in abundance and in other years will be completely neglected by the bees.

Heather. Two sorts of heather: Erica and Ling. They produce quite different nectar and quite different results in the consistency of the honey. Erica yields irregularly. Ling produces nearly every year and copiously every three or four years. The honey from this plant is quite unique being thixotropic in character. Many people regard it as the best of honeys.

Broom. A very valuable pollen source early in the year.

Gorse. This again is a very useful pollen plant yielding practically no nectar.

Old Man's Beard. This plant seems to be becoming more common and is proving a good source of pollen.

Lavender. Grown in many gardens. May be a valuable source of nectar in suburban areas.

Ivy. Nectar and pollen are given in abundance by this plant during the late autumn and early winter lasting, sometimes, well into November. When the weather is kind enough it provides a very useful fillip for nearby colonies.

Trees

Horsechestnut. Has an abundance of pollen (brick red in colour), very attractive and valuable to bees early in the year.

Top Fruit. Apples, pears, and stone fruit like plums give nectar and pollen. The nectar tends to be weak and usually not sufficient for the bees to gather any surplus from. However, the flowers are worked for their pollen much to the advantage of the fruit grower.

Lime. This tree yields well in some seasons when the trees become covered with many varieties of insects.

Oak. This tree is very susceptible to aphids. The sweet substance exuded by these creatures attracts the honeybee. Bees have also been known to work the flowers of this tree for pollen.

Sycamore. This tree is a good source of nectar in many areas. It can be unreliable in some years when the bees will ignore it.

Elm. A source of early pollen.

Hazel. This tree, in some areas, can provide the first source of pollen for the bees who work the lambs-tail catkins avidly.

Willow. This family of trees very rarely fails to produce copious quantities of pollen in early spring.

Planting for the bees

Although growing plants in a garden will have little or no effect on the amount of honey the bees will produce, the beekeeper can get many hours of enjoyment watching the bees working. The following is a list of some garden plants that are attractive to bees. It is of necessity short, but it will give enough variety to be of interest to the bee and the beekeeper.

Arbutus uneda
Berberis
Buddleia globosa
Buddleia davidii
Calluna
Cotoneaster
Erica
Mahonia aquifolium

Mahonia bealei
Rhus typhina
Rhus glabra
Ribes sanguineum
Rosmarinus officinalis
Salix
Symphoricarpus

Appendix D

Useful Addresses

Beekeeping equipment and hives :

Robert Lee (Bee Supplies) Ltd.,
Beehive Works,
George Street,
Uxbridge, Middx.

Steele and Brodie,
Bee Hive Works,
Wormit,
Fife, Scotland.

E. H. Taylor Ltd.,
Welwyn,
Herts., AL6 0AZ.

E. H. Thorne (Beehives) Ltd.,
Beehive Works,
Wragby,
Lincoln,
Lincs., LN3 5LA.

Journals :

Bee Craft (The monthly Journal of the British Beekeepers' Association)

Mrs. J. Nicholls,
21, West Way,
Copthorne Bank,
Crawley,
West Sussex, RH10 3QS.

Beekeepers' News (Quarterly Journal)

Editor: Paul Smith, Esq.,
E. H. Thorne (Beehives) Ltd.,
Wragby,
Lincoln, LN3 5LA.

British Bee Journal,
46, Queen Street,
Geddington,
Nr. Kettering,
Northants., NN14 1AZ.

Bee World (International Bee Research Association),

Hill House,
Gerrards Cross,
Bucks., SL9 0NR.

The Scottish Beekeeper (magazine of the Scottish Beekeeper's Association),

A. B. Ferguson, Esq.,
School House,
Kilpatrick, Fleming,
Lockerbie, Dumfriesshire,
Scotland, DG11 3AV.

Scottish Bee Journal,
R. N. H. Skilling, Esq.,
34, Rennie Street,
Kilmarnock,
Scotland.

Beekeeping (A West Country Journal),

The Editor,
20, Parkhurst Road,
Torquay,
Devon.

Beekeeping associations :

British Beekeepers'
Association,
Secretary: M. H. F. Coward,
Esq.,
Reg. Office: Royal
Agricultural Society of
England,
Show Ground,
Stoneleigh,
Warwickshire.

The Scottish Beekeepers'
Association,
The General Secretary,
26, The Meadows,
Berwick-on-Tweed,
Northumberland, TD15 1NY.

The International Bee
Research Association,
Hill House,
Gerrards Cross,
Bucks., SL9 0NR.

Welsh Beekeepers'
Association,
General Secretary,
Tyn-y-Berllan,
Builth, Wales.

The Central Association of
Beekeepers,
Hon. Secretary,
Long Reach,
Stockbury Valley,
Sittingbourne, Kent.

Beekeeping Advisory Services :

The Beekeeping Adviser,
The National Beekeeping
Unit,
Luddington Experimental
Horticultural Station,
Stratford-on-Avon,
Warwickshire.

Insurance :

Bee Diseases Insurance Ltd.,
Scheme 'A' Manager (for less
than twenty colonies)
S. W. Tammadge, Esq.,
30, Lavington Road,
Worthing,
Sussex.

Bee Diseases Insurance Ltd.,
Scheme 'B' Manager-Secretary
(for more than twenty colonies)
M. H. F. Coward, Esq.,
F.I.A.,
High Trees,
Dean Lane,
Merstham,
Surrey.

Index